THE CLOUD WALKER

He wanted to fly. He wanted to fly through the air like a bird. And that was heresy.

He was old enough to understand about heresy, young enough not to be terrified by it. The dominie who taught him and the neddy who took care of his spiritual discipline had spent much time expounding the diabolical nature of unlawful machines. They had succeeded not in instilling Kieron with a proper dread of machines but only with a secret fascination. Even at the age of five, Kieron knew that some day he would have to construct an unlawful machine in order to fly like a bird.

The Cloud
Walker

Edmund Cooper

CORONET BOOKS
Hodder Paperbacks Ltd., London

Copyright © 1973 by Edmund Cooper
First published by Hodder and Stoughton
Limited 1973
Coronet edition 1975

Printed and bound in Great Britain for
Coronet Books, Hodder Paperbacks Ltd,
St. Paul's House, Warwick Lane,
London, EC4P 4AH
by C. Nicholls & Company Ltd,
The Philips Park Press, Manchester

ISBN 0 340 19478 2

From 1811 to 1812 the Luddites destroyed stocking frames, steam power looms, and shearing machines throughout Nottinghamshire, Derbyshire, Leicestershire and Yorkshire, and their rioting broke out again in 1816. They derived their name from Ned Ludd, an idiot boy of Leicestershire, who, it is said, unable to catch someone who had been tormenting him, destroyed some stocking frames in a fit of temper (1779).

Everyman's Encyclopaedia
(1958 edition)

Part One

EARTHBOUND

I

WHEN KIERON WAS eight years old he was encouraged to spend much time in the company of his affianced bride, Petrina. Later, at the end of the age of innocence, they would not be permitted to be alone together until Kieron had attained his majority, had been released from his apprenticeship, and was thus able to fulfil his contractual obligations.

Kieron was apprenticed to Hobart, the painter. Already, the boy was allowed to clean brushes and to help with the stretching of canvas and the grinding of pigment. When he was ten years old he would go to live with Hobart so that he could attend upon his master at all times. Kieron looked forward to this time and also dreaded it. He was anxious to discover the mysteries of painting, the laws of perspective, the laws of harmony and the laws of proper representation; but he did not really want to be a painter. He wanted to fly. He wanted to fly through the air like a bird. And that was heresy.

He was old enough to understand about heresy, young enough not to be terrified by it. The dominie who taught him and the neddy who took care of his spiritual discipline had spent much time expounding the diabolical nature of unlawful machines. They had succeeded not in instilling Kieron with a proper dread of machines but only with a secret fascination. Even at the age of five, Kieron knew that some day he would have to construct an unlawful machine in order to fly like a bird.

Petrina was nice — for a girl. She was the daughter of Sholto, the smith. Because Kieron was affianced to

Petrina, he was allowed to watch Sholto at the forge. It was a great privilege. Some day, Kieron realised, he, too, would have to be able to work metal. He would have to be able to work metal to make the necessary parts for a flying machine. He asked many questions of Sholto. The smith, a huge, gentle man who took great pleasure in his work, saw no harm in talking to a small boy — especially one who was contracted to his daughter — and did not regard it as a breach of the oath of secrecy imposed by the Guild of Smiths. Soon Kieron had picked up a little of the lore of the tempering of steel, the fastening of plates by rivets, the shaping of helms, clasps, pikes, ploughshares.

"Boy," Sholto would say good-naturedly, "you are nought but a loon, an idler. Your thoughts should be of draughting and colouring, not of beating metals to your will. Go now and think on how to hold a charred twig steady to your design, or Master Hobart will make your arse somewhat tender."

Kieron was discreet. He knew when the smith joked or was earnest; and he knew also that it was wise not to mention his growing knowledge of the working of metals to anyone, and particularly his father.

The days of childhood are both long and short. Kieron would rise with his family at first light and, like them, carry out mechanically the routine tasks that were necessary before the real work of the day could begin. He would collect shavings and waste wood from his father's workshop for the fire, while his mother drew water from the well and set the porridge to boil, and while his father went out to seek game or to fell a tree to be stored against its seasoning. When the sun was its own width above the eastern rim of the world, the family would come together for breakfast. Porridge always, bread always, fat always, bacon sometimes, eggs sometimes — depending upon the state of the hens, the state of the pigs, the state of trade.

After breakfast, Kieron, along with a score of other children in the hill reaches of the seigneurie, would go to the dominie's house for an hour of instruction. After that, each boy would go to the house of his master, to serve at his apprenticeship until noon.

Kieron was luckier than most boys. Hobart was prosperous, having found much favour in the eyes of Fitzalan, Lord of the Seigneurie of Arundel. Hobart was strong on portraiture, and Fitzalan of Arundel was a vain man with a vain wife and three vain daughters. He still hoped for a son; but the daughters alone were more than enough to keep Hobart tolerably employed.

Hobart could afford to indulge Kieron, could afford to let the boy experiment with charcoal sticks and precious paper. Hobart had never married. Prosperous now, white-haired and lonely, he saw Kieron as the son he would have wished to beget had there been time. So the boy was indulged much and scolded little. Hobart discerned that he had a talent for line, but not as yet a great sense of colour. Well, perhaps it would come. Perhaps it would come. Hobart liked to think that his pictures and those of Kieron's would eventually hang side by side in the great hall of the castle, collecting the dust and the dignity of centuries . . .

The days of childhood are both long and short. In the afternoons, when Kieron had discharged his duties to Master Hobart, his time was his own. Such freedom was a luxury. It would end when he reached the age of ten and became a full apprentice. And after that, he realised, the freedom to do as he pleased would be gone from his life for ever. Unless he could change the destiny that had been chosen for him. He was young enough to believe that this was possible, old enough to realise that he would have to challenge established — almost sacred — traditions.

In the summer afternoons, he would go with Petrina to the woodlands of the downs — the ridge of hills that rose almost like a man-made barrier ten or twelve kilometres from the sea. There, on land that belonged to the roe deer, the pheasant and the rabbit, they would construct worlds of make-believe.

Petrina was a wide-eyed nervous girl, with hair the smokey colour of wheat that was overdue for harvesting. One day, Kieron would be her husband, the father of her children. Therefore she determined to learn about him. She already knew that he had a secret ambition; but she did not know what it was.

On a hot summer afternoon, partly by chance, partly by design, she learned what Kieron wanted to do most of all.

They had wearied of climbing trees, disturbing deer, picking wild flowers; and now they were resting on short, brilliantly green grass under an enormous beech tree, gazing up through its leaves at the sky.

"When you are a great painter," said Petrina, "I shall be able to buy beautiful fabrics and make dresses that will be the envy of every woman in the seigneurie."

"I shall never be a great painter," said Kieron without regret.

"You are apprenticed to Master Hobart. He is a great painter. You will learn his skills, and to them you will add your own."

"I shall never be as great as Master Hobart. He gave his life to it. I cannot give mine."

"Why?"

"Because, Petrina, there is something else I must do."

"There is nothing else you can do, Kieron. You are apprenticed to Master Hobart, and you and I are contracted for marriage. Such is our destiny."

"Such is our destiny," mimicked Kieron. "Stupid talk. The talk of a girl child. I want to fly."

"Don't you want to marry me?"

"I want to fly."

She sighed. "We are to be married. We shall be married. You will be a grand master of your art. And we shall have three children. And your greatest painting will be of a terrible fish that destroys men by fire. It is foretold. And there is nothing to be done about it."

Kieron was intrigued. "It is foretold?"

Petrina smiled. "Last summer, the astrologer, Marcus

12

of London, was summoned to the castle. Seigneur Fitzalan wished to know if his lady would ever bring forth a son."

"Well?"

"My father was commanded to repair the bearings of the stand for the astrologer's star glass. My mother persuaded Marcus to cast your horoscope in fee... So Kieron, the future is settled. You will be a grand master, and I shall bear three children... Listen to the bees! They dance mightily. If we can follow them, we can come back at dusk for the honey."

"Hang the bees!" exploded Kieron. "And hang the astrologer Marcus! I alone can decide my future. I shall complete my apprenticeship with Master Hobart. There is nothing I can do about that. Besides, he is a kind man, and a better master than most. Also, I like to draw. But when I am a man, things will be different. I shall be my own master. I shall choose my own future. And I choose to learn how to fly."

"Will you sprout wings?"

"I shall construct a flying machine."

Petrina turned pale. "A flying machine. Kieron, be careful. It is all right to speak of such things to me. I shall be your wife. I shall bear your children. But do not talk of flying machines to anyone else, especially the dominie and the neddy."

Kieron pressed her hand, and lay back on the bright green grass and stared upwards through the leaves of the beech tree. "I am not a fool," he said. "The dominie is like the neddy, in that his mind is stiff with rules and habits. But the dominie is just a weak old man, whereas the neddy —"

"Whereas the neddy could have you burned at the stake," cut in Petrina sharply.

"They don't burn children now. Even you should know that."

"But they still burn men, and one day you will be a man. They burned a farmer at Chichester two summers ago for devising a machine to cut his wheat... Kieron, for my sake, try not to think about flying machines. Such thoughts are far too dangerous."

Kieron let out a great sigh. "All the exciting things are dangerous... Look at the sky through the leaves. So blue, so beautiful. And when the white clouds pass, don't you wish you could reach up and touch them? They are like islands, great islands in the sky. One day I shall journey among those islands. One day I shall reach out and touch the clouds as I pass by."

Petrina shivered. "You make me feel cold with this wild talk."

"I make myself feel cold also. The First Men had flying machines, Petrina. Silver birds that roared like dragons and passed high over the clouds. The dominie says so. Even the neddy will admit to that. It is history."

"The First Men destroyed themselves," retorted Petrina.

"So did the Second Men," said Kieron tranquilly. "They also had flying machines; though not, perhaps, as good as those of the First Men. It must have been wonderful to pass across the skies at great speed, to look down upon the earth and see men go about their tasks like insects."

"Men are not insects!"

"From a great height, all living things must seem like insects."

"The First Men destroyed themselves. So did the Second Men. That, too, is history. The neddies are right. Machines are evil."

Kieron laughed. "Machines have no knowledge of good and evil. Machines cannot think. Only men can think."

"Then," said Petrina, "too much thinking is evil — especially when it is about forbidden things."

Suddenly Kieron felt strangely old, strangely protective. He said: "Don't worry, little one. I shall not think too much. Very likely, you will have three children, as the astrologer says... I know where there is a plum tree. Shall we see if there are any ripe enough to eat?"

14

Petrina jumped up. "I know where there is an apple tree. The high ones are already turning red."

Kieron laughed. "Plums and apples! Let us drive all gloomy thoughts away with plums and apples."

Hand in hand, they walked out of the glade, out into the rich gold splendour of late summer sunshine.

2

ON HIS TENTH birthday, Kieron ate his farewell breakfast with all the solemnity required for the occasion. Then he shook hands with Gerard, his father, and kissed Kristen, his mother, once on each cheek. It was only a ritual farewell because they would still see each other frequently. But it was the symbolic end of Kieron's childhood. He would sleep no more in the house of his father.

Gerard said: "Son, you will attend Master Hobart in all his needs. He will impart his skills to you. In years to come, your paintings will adorn the walls of the castle. Maybe, they will also hang in the great houses of London, Bristol, Brum. Then, perhaps, your mother and I will not have lived in vain."

"Sir," said Kieron, forcing back the tears that came to his eyes for no apparent reason, "I will learn from Master Hobart all that I may. I will try to be worthy of you. I would have been a joiner like you, had it been your pleasure. But, since you wished me to make likenesses, I will paint portraits that will not shame the father of Kieron Joinerson."

Kristen held him close and said: "You have three shirts, three vests and two pair of leggings. You have a lambskin jacket and good boots. These I have packed in the deerhide bag. Keep warm, Kieron, eat well. We — we love you and shall watch your progress."

He sensed that she, too, was miserable. He could not understand why. It was supposed to be an important and joyful occasion for all concerned.

"I will see you soon, mother." He smiled, trying to cheer himself up as well.

"Ay, but you will not lie again in the bed your father made for you. You will not curl up under the sheets I wove and the down quilt I made before you were born."

"Enough, Kristen," said Gerard. "You will have us all whimpering like babies." He looked at his wife and was aware of the white streaks in her hair, the lines etched on her face. She was twenty-eight years old; but her back was still straight and her breasts were high. She had worn well.

Kieron picked up the deerhide bag. Suddenly, the sense of occasion was upon him, and he felt very formal. "Good day to you, then, my parents. Thank you for giving me the breath of life. Thank you for filling my belly in summer and in winter. Ludd rest you both."

Kristen fled into her kitchen, sobbing. Gerard raised a great hairy arm to his forehead, as he often did in his workshop, and wiped away sweat that did not exist.

"Ludd be with you, my son. Go now to Master Hobart. As I am the best joiner in fifty kilometres marching, so you will become the best painter within a thousand kilometres."

"Father, I want to —" Kieron stopped. It had been on the tip of his tongue to say: I do not want to be a painter. I want to learn how to fly.

"Yes, Kieron?"

"I — I want to be worthy of you and to make you proud."

Gerard laughed and slapped his shoulder playfully. "Be off with you, changeling. From now on, you will eat better food than we have been able to give you."

"I doubt that it will taste as good." There was more he wanted to say. Much more. But the words stuck in his throat. Kieron went out of the cottage and began to walk along the track that led down to Arundel. He did not look back, but he knew that Gerard was standing at the door watching him. He did not look back because there was a disturbing impulse to run to his father and tell him what he really wanted to do.

It was a fine October morning. The sky was blue; but a thick carpet of mist lay over the low land stretching away to the sea. Arundel lay beneath the mist; but the castle, its grey stone wet with dew and shining in the morning light, sat on the hillside clear above the mist. A faerie castle, bright, mysterious, full of unseen power.

There was a saying: those who live in the shadow of the castle shall prosper or burn. Master Hobart had a house under the very battlements. He had prospered. Kieron hoped that he, too, would prosper. Only a fool would risk burning. Only a fool would want to build a flying machine.

High in the sky a buzzard circled gracefully. Kieron put down his bag and watched it. Such effortless movements, such freedom. He envied the bird. He envied its freedom, its effortless mastery of the air.

"Some day, buzzard," said Kieron, "I shall be up there with you. I shall be higher. I shall look down on you. You will know that a man has invaded your world. You will know that men have reconquered the sky."

Still, this was no time to make speeches that no one would hear, and particularly speeches that no one should hear. Master Hobart, doubtless, would be waiting and impatient. Kieron bent down to pick up his bag.

He saw a dandelion, a dandelion clock. A stem with a head full of seeds. He plucked the stem, lifted the head and blew. Seeds drifted away in the still, morning air. Seeds supported by the gossamer threads that resisted their fall to earth.

Kieron watched, fascinated. A few of the seeds, caught by an indetectible current of warm air, rose high and were lost against the morning sunlight. Even dandelion seeds could dance in the air. It was humiliating that man should be earthbound.

Kieron remembered that, on this day of days, Hobart would be waiting to welcome him with some ceremony.

He sighed, picked up the deerhide bag and marched resolutely towards Arundel. Ahead of him there would be months and years wherein he would have to master all the secrets of Hobart's craft. But when he was a man, when the apprenticeship had been served with honour, that would be the time to learn to fly.

Meanwhile, there was always the time to dream.

3

WINTER CAME, TURNING the land bleak, capping the downs with freezing mist, weaving a delicate tracery of frost over trees, grass, hedgerows and the walls of houses, bringing ice patches on the placid Arun river, making the air sharp as an English apple wine.

Hobart coughed much and painted little in the winter. The rawness ate into his bones, brought pains to his chest. He spent much time sitting by a log fire with a shawl or sheepskin round his shoulders, brooding upon projects that he would undertake in the spring. There was the mural for the great hall to consider; and Seigneur Fitzalan had commissioned a symbolic work, depicting the fall of the First Men, to the greater glory of Ludd, and for the Church of the Sacred Hammer.

Widow Thatcher, who cleaned house for Master Hobart and cooked for him, made many nourishing stews of rabbit or pheasant or lamb or venison with parsnips, mushrooms, carrots, potatoes, and the good black pepper for which Seigneur Fitzalan paid exorbitant sums to the skippers of windjammers that sailed as far as the Spice Islands.

Master Hobart would take but a few spoonfuls of the lovingly made stews. Then he would cough somewhat and draw shivering to the fire. Kieron, waiting properly until his master had finished eating, would gorge himself until his belly swelled and he felt the need to walk off his excess of eating in the frosty downs.

Though Hobart himself was idle during the dark months, he did not allow his young apprentice to remain idle. He instructed Kieron in the art of making fine charcoal sticks from straight twigs of willow, in the mysteries of fabric printing, in the newly fashionable art of collage, and in the ancient disciplines of colour binding and the preparation of a true canvas. He was even prepared to expend precious whale oil in the lamps so that on a dull afternoon Kieron would have enough light to sketch chairs, tables, bowls of fruit, hanging pheasants, and even the protesting Widow Thatcher.

Master Hobart was a white-haired old man, nearing his three score. The pains in his chest warned him that the summers left to him would not reach double figures. But he was stubbornly determined to live at least the eight years Kieron needed to complete his apprenticeship. Ludd permitting, he would see the boy established before he was lowered into the flinty earth of Sussex.

He permitted himself a small heresy — only a very small one, which surely Ludd would excuse. He permitted himself the secret delusion that Kieron was his natural son. Hobart had never lain with a woman. His art had been enough. But now he felt the need of a son; and Kieron, a boy with bright eyes and a quick mind, was all that a man could desire.

So Kieron escaped many of the usual rigours of apprenticeship. He was well fed, he had much freedom; and Hobart slipped many a silver penny into his purse.

Kieron understood the relationship very clearly. He loved the old man and did not object to the presumptions of a second father. Besides, Hobart was a great source of knowledge, and knowledge was what Kieron desired above everything.

In the evenings, before Hobart retired to an early bed, he and Kieron would sit, staring into the log fire, discerning images and fantasies, talking of many things. Hobart drank somewhat — to alleviate the pains and the coughing — of usquebaugh, or akvavit, or eau de vie, depending on which brigantines had recently traded with the seigneurie. In his cups at night, he was prepared to discuss that which he would shun sober in the morning. He was prepared to talk about the First Men and the Second Men. He was even prepared to talk about machines.

"Master Hobart, the dominie says that the First Men choked on their own cleverness. What does he mean by that?"

"Pah!" Hobart sipped his usquebaugh and felt the warmth tingle pleasantly through his limbs. "Dominie Scrivener should teach you more of letters and the mysteries of nature and the casting of numbers than of the First Men."

"Yesterday, when I was making a picture of this house as it stands below the castle, and represented the roughness of the flint walls, you said I was clever. Is cleverness a bad thing? Shall I, too, choke on it?"

"Peace, boy. Let me think. It seems I must not only instruct you in matters of art, but in matters of the world, and in proper thinking." More usquebaugh. More warmth. More coughing. "What the dominie says is true. The First Men did choke on their own cleverness. They made the air of their cities unfit to breathe, they made the waters of their rivers and lakes unfit to drink, they covered good farming land with stone and metal causeways, at times they even made the sea turn black. All this they did with the machines they worshipped insanely. And, as if that were not enough, they devised terrible machines whose sole purpose was to destroy people by the hundred, by the thousand, even by the ten thousand. Missiles, they were called: machines that leapt through the sky with their cargoes of death. Ay, the dominie was right. They choked on their own cleverness ... But your cleverness, Kieron is something different. You are clever in an honest art, not in the love of mechanisms that destroy the hand that creates them."

"Must all machines be bad?" asked Kieron.

"Yes, Kieron, all machines are evil. The Divine Boy understood that a thousand years ago, when machines first began to corrupt this fair land. That is why he

22

attacked them with his hammer. But the people would not listen; and so he was taken and crucified."

There was silence for a while; silence punctuated by the crackling of logs on the hearth, and by Master Hobart noisily sipping his usquebaugh.

At length, Kieron grew bold. "It is said that Seigneur Fitzalan has a clock in the castle. A clock that goes tick-tock and tells the hours, minutes and very seconds of the day. A clock is a machine, isn't it, Master Hobart? Is a clock evil?"

The usquebaugh made Master Hobart splutter somewhat. It was a while before he could make his reply. "I see that neither the dominie nor the neddy have shed as much light on this matter as they ought. It is true, Kieron, that a clock is a machine; but for the great ones of our world, who have many matters to attend to and little enough time to deal with their affairs, a clock is a *necessary* machine. Holy Church makes much distinction between necessary machines, which are proper, and unnecessary machines which are improper. So Seigneur Fitzalan's clock, which I have seen many times and which is a most marvellous thing — executed, so they say, by the best horologist in Paris — is a proper machine. There is no record that the Divine Boy ever attacked clocks."

Kieron noted how much usquebaugh had been taken, and asked the question he would not have dared to ask in the light of a sober morning.

"Master Hobart, did the Divine Boy ever attack flying machines?"

"Flying machines?" Master Hobart was puzzled. "There are no flying machines."

"No, sir. But once there were." Kieron was sweating. The fire, certainly, was warm; but his backside was cold. Nevertheless, Kieron was sweating. "You, yourself, have told me of the missiles; and I have heard that once there were winged machines that transported people through the air, across the seas, from land to land, at great speed.

That is why I ask if the Divine Boy ever attacked flying machines."

"Ludd save us all!" Master Hobart scratched his head. "Flying machines! My history serves me ill. But, Kieron, boy, I think they came long after Ned Ludd. I think they came when the First Men had utterly abandoned the ways of righteousness. I think they came but a hundred years, perhaps two hundred years, before the great destruction."

Kieron gazed at the level of usquebaugh in the flask of green glass, and decided to press his luck. "They say that even the Second Men had flying machines. Surely, if such machines were used not to destroy people but to take them wherever they wished to go, they could not be evil?"

Master Hobart rolled his eyes, tried to focus, took another drink and again failed to focus. He scratched his head. "They were evil, Kieron. What is to prevent men walking or riding across the land? What is to prevent them from sailing across the oceans? Men do not need to take to the air. *Quod erat demonstrandum.* Therefore machines which lift men into the sky are evil."

Kieron took a deep breath. "Some day, I shall construct a flying machine. It will not be used for evil purposes, only for good."

Master Hobart stood up, swayed a little, gazed down at his apprentice hazily. "You will paint, Kieron. You will paint well. Ludd protect you from fantastic dreams. Help me to my chamber."

4

AT FIFTEEN KIERON was a boy worth looking at. Master Hobart's spoiling and Widow Thatcher's prodigious cooking had given him height and broad shoulders and self-confidence. He looked more like a young farmer or hunter than a painter's apprentice. At Midsummer's Night Fair, he could run, jump, wrestle or hurl the javelin with the best of the young men in the seigneurie; though Master Hobart winced greatly and comforted himself with French spirit when he saw Kieron leap seven metres along the sand pit and come down like a rolling ball, or when the boy's hand was held in a wrestler's lock and the joints could be heard to crack noisily under pressure. He was not afraid for Kieron's neck, only for his fingers. What kind of an artist would the boy become with broken fingers?

But Kieron was a golden boy and seemed to bear a charmed life. More than ever, Master Hobart thought of him as a blood son. Indeed, in a fit of stupidity, he had even gone to see Gerard the joiner and his wife Kristen, offering them one thousand schilling if they would surrender their blood claim for all time.

Gerard grew red in the face, and spoke more loudly and less courteously than he ought to one who had entry to the castle and the ear of the seigneur. Kristen, as was the way with women, wept somewhat, shrieked somewhat and uttered strange accusations for which Gerard promptly commanded her to apologise. Hobart was greatly embarrassed by the whole venture. He found himself apologising also, profusely and at some length. In the end, he managed to enjoin Gerard and Kristen — good, honest people for whom he professed the greatest esteem et cetera — to say nothing of the matter to Kieron.

The next day, he sent Gerard a dagger of Spanish steel, and Kristen ten metres of Irish linen. He also sent them an imaginative picture of Ned Ludd raising his immortal hammer against the weaving machines. It was the first truly satisfactory composition in oils that Kieron had executed. It was signed Kieron app Hobart; and it was one of the most precious things that Hobart possessed.

Kieron's skill in art was now all that Hobart could desire in a boy of his age. His strength still lay in line — the master was amazed at the boldness and confidence of his strokes — but he had begun to develop the true, authentic feeling for colour and texture that is the hallmark of a great painter. Also, his mastery of the mechanics of his art was phenomenal. He could mix pigment and oil to achieve a true and beautiful primary. Also, without any help from Hobart, he had devised two methods of obtaining a purer flax seed oil. The first was elegantly simple: it consisted only of waiting. The oil was stored in jars until its impurities settled in a layer at the bottom. Then, not content with the purity achieved in this manner, Kieron would add caustic soda, which settled out any suspended matter still remaining. The result was a completely pure flax seed oil, clear, warm, golden. Perfect for the use of an artist.

Hobart was astounded by this. Previously he had used the oil as it came from the flax growers, with minute particles that muddied its translucence. But Kieron's refined oil, as he called it, was surely a gift of Ludd, in that it did not pollute the pigments or harden too quickly upon the canvas. Hobart was convinced that no painter in England could have a finer oil base than that discovered by Kieron.

He asked the boy how he had devised such methods of purification. The answer was not greatly enlightening.

"You always complained of the quality of the colours

we use," said Kieron. "The pigments were true, so clearly the fault lay in the oil. I poured oil into a clear flask and gazed at it. I could see nothing wrong. But I let the oil stand and came back to it the following day. Still I could see nothing wrong. But on the second day, I discovered that the bottom of the flask was covered with fine particles. Again, I let it stand. Seven days later, there was a sediment, and the oil was more clear. Then I understood the need for patience."

"But the caustic soda. How did you understand that the caustic soda would give yet greater clarity?"

"I didn't," Kieron smiled. "It seemed to me that the process of depositing impurities might not yet be over. So I experimented."

"You experimented?" Hobart was shaken. Experiment was but a hair's breadth from heresy.

Kieron was unperturbed. "I experimented with the addition of salt, with the addition of vinegar, with the addition of weak soda and with the addition of strong soda. I would have experimented with many other substances, too, had they been easy to obtain."

"Boy," said Hobart, "you frighten me."

Kieron laughed. "Sometimes, sir, I frighten myself ... The flax seed oil is to your liking?"

"It is a great oil, Kieron. We could make a fortune by selling it to painters throughout the land."

"Then, Master Hobart, do not sell my refined oil. Use it only yourself, and be the greatest painter of our time."

Tears came to Hobart's eyes. He was not much given to weeping, except when the coughing spasms tore him apart. "You truly wish to keep this clear oil for my use only?"

Kieron smiled. "Sir, I could not wish for a better master. But is it not possible to establish both fame and fortune? If you use the refined oil until — until you no longer choose to paint, you will be known far and wide for the purity of your colour. Then would be the time to sell refined oil, when you are already too high to fear rivalry."

Hobart induced a fit of coughing, as an excuse for the tears he could no longer conceal. "Boy, I see that you love me, and I am proud. I see also that you are touched by greatness, and I am again proud, but also terrified ... Kieron, humour an old man. The refined oil is truly marvellous. But do not experiment rashly. The church ... The church likes new ideas little. I would commend discretion to you."

"I think perhaps all experiment is rash," answered Kieron, "but my mind will not rest ... However, I will be discreet. I would not wish to shame you or my parents."

These days, Kieron did not see a great deal of Petrina. The times when they could go up on to the downs alone together seemed very long ago. Now, they met socially only in the company of their elders. They saw each other chiefly at the Church of the Sacred Hammer, at the fairs of the four seasons, and on holy days, when all work ceased and folk ventured out in their best clothes to visit relatives or friends or to promenade in the castle grounds listening to Seigneur Fitzalan's musicians.

Sometimes Kieron and Petrina met accidentally in the street, but they could not stay long to talk to each other for fear of the mischievous wagging of tongues. As Kieron had grown in stature, so Petrina had grown in beauty — or so it seemed. Her hair stretched below her waist in a long luxuriant plait. There was blue fire in her eyes, and her lips were hauntingly full. The freckles had gone, the boyish figure had gone, and the curves of a woman swelled pleasingly upon her. Kieron, normally full of confidence and self-assurance, became tongue-tied in her presence. But, without looking, he knew when she was watching him at the games; and her presence lent a curious strength. In three more years she would be his wife. Truly, his father had contracted well with Sholto the Smith.

Kieron made sketches from memory of Petrina, which he hung on the wall by his bed. Hobart inspected them and said nothing. The boy's artistic discipline went to pieces when he dealt with this particular subject. But the results were curiously exciting, enough to make the blood sing. There was one sketch of the girl climbing in what was, presumably, a beech tree. Somehow, Kieron had managed to make the girl look naked while being properly clothed. The technique was rough; but the sketch had great impact. It smacked of heresy. The church had never approved of nakedness. And yet she was fully clothed. And yet she seemed naked. Hobart hoped that the neddy would never see this sketch. He scratched his head and seriously wondered if he should summon an astrologer to conjure against daemons.

But preoccupation with dream images of Petrina did not distract Kieron unduly from his obsession with the conquest of the air. Over the years he had conscientiously studied all things — however great or small — that had some freedom of movement through the air: clouds, birds, insects, drifting seeds, even autumn leaves. On summer afternoons, when there was no great urgency of work and when Master Hobart was content to doze in the sun, Kieron would lie back on the sweet-smelling grass and feel the pull of earth, the flexible and invisible band that constantly tried to draw him to the centre of the world. And he would look up at white clouds drifting lazily across the sky, at larks soaring, at swallows cutting the air magically as with a knife, at butterflies that seemed to nervously jump across unseen stepping stones, at dragon-flies hovering.

It seemed absurd that so great a creature as man was tied down. Once, so it was said, man had even ventured upon the surface of the moon. Kieron did not entirely believe the legend; but it was known beyond any shadow of doubt that men had once enjoyed the freedom of the sky. They would do so again, of that Kieron was sure — whatever the priests of Ludd might say.

Meanwhile, it was pleasant, if tantalising, to watch the great clouds scud, to know that they were made of water, which was heavier than air, and yet could still float high in the azure reaches. And it was pleasant, if tantalising, to watch a bird of prey hover, circle, and with little or no wing movement rise higher and higher until it became a speck.

Kieron contrasted such effortless movement with the phrenetic motions of the bee, beating its wings so fast in order to stay aloft that they became invisible, though the sound of the tiny membranes was at times as he imagined that of a great engine of the old days.

Truly, the mysteries of being airborne were profound. Truly there must be many different ways of conquering the sky.

Kieron began to experiment with kites. Kites were permitted by the neddies. Kites were not defined as machines but as toys. Many of the children in the seigneurie flew kites. It was considered a harmless thing to do. But it was also considered eccentric in a young man of fifteen, with a bare three years of apprenticeship left; a young man whose mind should now be focussing on more serious matters.

Elders raised their eyebrows when they saw Kieron standing on the green on blustery autumn afternoons, solemnly reeling out string for a kite that climbed higher than any before it. They marvelled not at the height achieved by Kieron but at the indulgence of Master Hobart. Surely the old painter was in his dotage, or Seigneur Fitzalan was displeased with his work, else he would find much for idle young hands to do.

Kieron's contemporaries were less passive in their reaction. They made great fun of him, which he bore patiently. They thought him witless, and called him Kieron-head-in-the-air because he always seemed to be gazing upwards. Aylwin, apprenticed to the miller, went further.

Aylwin, a broad-set strong young man of Kieron's own

age, had always envied him. For two reasons. Aylwin had never wanted to become a miller. From childhood he had been obsessed by drawing and painting. More than anything, he would have liked to be apprenticed to Master Hobart. Also, there was the matter of Petrina. Aylwin was contracted to Joan, daughter of Lodowick, the saddler. Joan, at best, was a dumpy girl, lacking grace. True, she would bear children well, and she was versed in the womanly arts. But she was not the kind of girl to make a young man's heart beat noisily inside his breast.

Aylwin could have forgiven Kieron for being apprenticed to Master Hobart. Or he could have forgiven him for being contracted to Petrina. But he could not forgive him for both. So, one afternoon when a kite newly designed by Kieron had risen exceedingly high, and when Kieron, impervious to the taunts of his fellows, continued to manoeuvre it yet higher, Aylwin threw discretion to the winds, rushed upon the green and cut the cord that held the kite. The wind was high. The kite swung crazily for a moment or two, then it drifted south towards the sea.

Kieron gazed at Aylwin in perplexity. "Why did you do that?"

"Because you are a fool."

"Do I not have a right to foolishness, if it is my pleasure?"

Aylwin was appalled at his own stupidity, but there was no going back.

"No. You should be as the rest of us. Kite-flying is for children. We are beyond childish things."

"You are not beyond a beating," said Kieron. "There was much thought in the design of my kite. For that you shall pay."

"Try me!" shouted Aylwin. "Try me!" But he did not feel over confident. He had greater strength than Kieron. That he knew. But Kieron had suppleness of limbs and suppleness of mind. A formidable combination.

31

"Aylwin," said Kieron quietly, "you have earned some chastisement. I am sorry."

The two young men faced each other; Aylwin confident of strength but not of tactics, Kieron confident of tactics but not of strength.

Aylwin rushed in. If he could come to close grips with Kieron, that would be an end of it.

He rushed in, but Kieron did not wait to receive him. He gave a mighty leap over Aylwin's head. Alywin stopped his charge and turned round — only to receive both of Kieron's feet in his face — a magnificent flying kick to the jaw.

Aylwin saw stars. The world darkened, and he fell down. But sight returned, and he looked up to see Kieron waiting patiently for him. With a cry of rage Aylwin leaped to his feet. Again he rushed at Kieron, prepared this time for some evasive action. There was none. Kieron seemed determined to take the charge on his shoulder, a stupid thing to do in view of Aylwin's superior weight. But, at the last moment, with splendid timing, Kieron bent. Aylwin could not stop the charge and sprawled helplessly over Kieron's back. As he did so, Kieron straightened; and Aylwin executed a full turn high in the air then landed flat on his back with a jarring thud. He tried to get up, and could not. His head ached, there was a great roaring in his ears and pain in every part of his body.

Kieron stood above him. "Are you sorry for cutting the cord, Aylwin?"

"Ludd damn you!" He snatched feebly at Kieron's leg.

Kieron trod on his arm, pinning it down. "Are you sorry?"

Aylwin whimpered with pain. "Damn you to hell and back. I will never be sorry. You have Master Hobart, and you will have Petrina. May Ludd strike me if ever..." Aylwin fainted.

When he returned to consciousness, he found that Kieron was gently slapping his face.

"Leave me alone, fellow. I am all right, and I will never be sorry. You may break my bones, Kieron-head-in-the-air, but I will never be sorry. I swear it."

Kieron lifted him gently to a sitting position, then crouched by him. "Why did you speak of Master Hobart and Petrina?"

Aylwin gazed up, white-faced. "You have all that I ever wanted," he sobbed. "And yet you play like a child!"

Suddenly Kieron understood. "You wanted to paint?"

"Yes! Ludd's death, I wanted to paint. But I shall only ever grind corn."

"And you desire to be wed with Petrina?"

Aylwin grimaced. "Be amused. You know I am contracted to Joan."

Kieron said simply: "Forgive me. I did not know the forces."

"You did not know the forces?" Aylwin looked at him uncomprehendingly.

"I did not know the forces that drove you to cut the cord . . . There is nothing we can do about Petrina. I will wed with her. I love her. But, perhaps, there is something we can do about the other . . ."

"There is nothing to be done about it," said Aylwin. "A miller does not paint, a miller's apprentice does not paint. That is all there is to it."

Kieron smiled. "There is a law against it? Seigneur Fitzalan has proclaimed that all millers who daub canvas shall be put to death?"

Aylwin said: "You mock me . . . Besides, who would instruct me? Who would give me canvas and paint?"

"I would."

Aylwin's mouth fell open. He did not speak for fully a minute. "You would! Why?"

"Is there cause for a feud between us, Aylwin? Must we be enemies because of decisions that were not of our taking?"

"No, but —"

"Hear me, then. I would have you as my friend. One

day I may need such a friend. In the matter of Petrina, I can and will do nothing. But Master Hobart loves me, and I serve him well. He will give me canvas and pigments and will not ask questions that I do not wish to answer . . . I will instruct you, Aylwin. I will pass on the skills that are passed on to me. Is that enough?"

Aylwin held out his hand and gripped Kieron's forearm. Kieron returned the gesture, thus sealing the ancient pact of mutual loyalty.

"It is enough," said Aylwin. "By the hammer of Ludd, it is more than enough. But why do you do this thing?"

"We have clasped each other, and so we are bound each to the other. It is agreed?"

"It is agreed."

"Then I can tell you certain things, Aylwin. You wish to paint, but are destined to become a miller. I wish to construct flying machines, but I am destined to become a painter. Separately, we must accept our fates. Together we may overcome them. Are you truly with me?"

"To the death. But, as you say, it is not unlawful for a miller to paint. On the other hand, flying machines — machines of any kind — are unlawful. You have a bleak future, Kieron-head-in-the-air."

Kieron smiled at the taunt, which now contained no malice. "Men make laws. Men may change them . . . The kite whose cord was cut was not just a childish toy, Aylwin. It was an experiment. It was an experimental design for a man-lifting kite."

"Do not proceed. The neddies will burn you."

"Hear me. I have discovered an idea, which, when the time is ripe, will prevent the neddies from doing anything."

"What is the idea?"

"Historical necessity," said Kieron. "It will be necessary, sooner or later, for man to take to the air once more. Meanwhile, I must work secretly. I must be ready for that time."

"I fear for you, Kieron."

34

"I fear for myself, Aylwin. But, we have a bargain, you and I. I will share my skills with you, and you will be content."

"What will you require of me, in exchange?"

"I don't know. Truly, I don't know. At some time, almost certainly, I shall require your help. The risks may be high. They may be high enough even to hazard your life. But I shall try to avoid that."

Aylwin stood up. So did Kieron. They clasped forearms once again, in affirmation.

"Better a dead painter than a live miller," joked Aylwin.

"Better by far a live painter and a live man of the air," said Kieron.

5

MISTRESS ALYX FITZALAN was seventeen years old and the bane of Seigneur Fitzalan's life. Within the year, thank Ludd, she would be wed with the young Seigneur Talbot of Chichester. As far as Seigneur Fitzalan was concerned, it could not happen too soon. He wished Talbot joy of her, but doubted greatly that any joy would come of the union. Still, it was politically necessary for the Talbots and the Fitzalans to stand side by side. Between them, they controlled much of the southern coastline. Which was convenient in times of peace and doubly convenient in times of war. Which Ludd forbid.

Alyx knew that she was destined to be a sacrificial lamb and conducted herself accordingly. As Fitzalan's eldest daughter, she had many privileges. As the key to his control of a large segment of the coast, she realised that, until Fitzalan had a copy of the marriage vows in his strong box, she could demand anything within reason.

She did, frequently. She demanded entertainments, feasts, diversions. It was well known that Talbot of Chichester was a sickly young man who bled frequently from the nose. Alyx had spies who told her that he was not long for this world. Though she loathed him, she hoped he would live long enough to wed her and get a son. By this means, Alyx dreamed of equalling her father in his power.

Meanwhile, she held Fitzalan in thrall. He could not risk her rejection of the contract.

She was a great horsewoman. She loved horses, it seemed, more than anything else.

What more natural than that she should require a portrait of herself on horseback leaping a seven-bar gate?

Alyx already had five portraits of herself. Two hung in the castle, one had been sent to London, and two had been given to Talbot.

Master Hobart had painted all five portraits. At the suggestion of the sixth, he held up his shaking hands in horror.

"Seigneur Fitzalan, how shall I catch your daughter on horseback leaping a seven-bar gate?"

"I know not, Master Hobart, nor do I care," retorted Seigneur Fitzalan calmly. "But it is the price of peace — at least for a time — and I will have it done."

"But, Seigneur —"

"No buts, master painter. See to it. And see to it also that the horse is no less graceful than its rider. I have a fine stable, and those who see your picture should know it."

"Yes, Seigneur."

"Be still, man! You shake like an autumn leaf. I trust you will not shake so when the brush is in your hand."

"No, Seigneur," assured Hobart hastily. "It is but a tremor of agitation. When I hold the brush, my hand is rock steady."

"If it be steady enough to make good likenesses of both horse and rider, I will put five hundred schilling into it."

"Thank you, Seigneur."

Fitzalan frowned and stared hard at the old man. "But, if the canvas be not to my liking, you shall eat it."

"Yes, Seigneur. Thank you." Master Hobart retreated from the presence, bowing many times, his hands clasped tightly together (partly to stop them trembling) as if with intense gratitude, like one whose execution has just been stayed — if only temporarily.

"Hobart!"

"Seigneur?"

"A word. And stop bobbing up and down, man. You make me nervous."

"Forgive me, Seigneur." Hobart froze.

"This picture . . . Start soon, Master Hobart, but do not hurry. You follow me?"

"Yes, Seigneur," said Hobart blindly. Though he did not.

Fitzalan explained. "Mistress Alyx is a dutiful and loving daughter, but she is also — how shall I put it? — impetuous if not actually headstrong."

"Just so, Seigneur."

"No, not just so. Damnation! Don't you understand what I'm saying?"

"Yes, Seigneur. All in the seigneurie know that Mistress Alyx is —"

"Hobart, you are a foolish old man, and you know nothing of womenfolk."

"Yes, Seigneur."

Suddenly, Fitzalan recalled that Hobart was indeed a foolish old man who knew nothing of womenfolk. "Hobart, forgive me. I treat you ill, old friend."

"You do me too much honour, Seigneur."

Fitzalan smiled. "Because we are friends, I will confide in you. Mistress Alyx, Ludd bless her, has curious notions. She needs interests, diversions. And for women, Hobart, diversions come costly. This picture, now. You could do it in a week, could you not?"

"Well, Seigneur, I —"

"Could you or could you not?"

"Yes, Seigneur."

"The very point. You will not do it in a week, Master Hobart. You will not even do it in a month. You will take time, much time. You will require many sketches, many sittings or whatever. Many long sittings. I make myself clear?"

"Yes, Seigneur."

"Mistress Alyx will scold you. I will scold you. But you will not hurry. I make myself clear?"

"Yes, Seigneur."

"Mistress Alyx is burdened by time, Hobart. She does not know this, but it is so. Therefore you will consume as much of her time as possible, without appearing to so do.... This prentice of yours — has he his wits about him?"

"Ay, Seigneur." Here, Hobart felt on firm ground. "A most intelligent and resourceful young man, and of great talent also with brush, chalk, pencil, crayon, char —"

"Enough. You need not declaim his battle honours. I have seen him about the castle, Hobart, and about the seigneurie. He is a pleasant young fellow.... Yes, he is a pleasant young fellow. Have him attend Mistress Alyx, Hobart. Have him ride with her, have him walk with her. Have him make enough — what the devil do you call them?"

"Preliminary studies," ventured Hobart.

"Have him make enough preliminary studies, sketches, or whatever the fellow does, to take up a full two-month of the wretched girl's forenoons, ay, and her afternoons also. Can this be done?"

"What of Mistress Alyx, Seigneur? She may weary —"

"Damn the Mistress Alyx! Women do not weary of being looked at nor of artists limning with devotion.... Seven hundred and fifty schilling, Hobart, and not a penny more. You have heard my requirements. Go now."

Hobart began his retreat once more, hands clasped tightly, the sweat dripping from his forehead.

Now he had two additional worries that would take much drowning in Scottish or French spirit. Mistress Alyx was a woman of some temperament. Also, Hobart realised with sad clarity that he had never been much good at horses.

6

MISTRESS ALYX DROVE Kieron to distraction. She was a wild young lady. Wild, beautiful, imperious, bored. Also intelligent. She was intelligent enough to realise that Kieron had been sent to her as a propitiatory sacrifice, a kind of whipping boy. Nevertheless, it amused her to apply the whip — verbally, emotionally, physically.

The first morning that Kieron presented himself with charcoal sticks, papers, drawing board, she allowed him to make a sketch while she offered barbed comment on his appearance, his dress, his accent, his ancestry, his lack of learning.

Kieron set up his drawing board and went to work. But after a few minutes, his hand was shaking, and the lines were terrible, and he knew it. So did Mistress Alyx.

Kieron's mission had been explained to him carefully and apologetically by Master Hobart.

"You see, my son," Hobart had begun to lapse into this form of address more and more, "there are diplomatic considerations in this commission. Seigneur Fitzalan was quite explicit. He requires Mistress Alyx to be distracted for a while. I am too old for such things. Therefore—"

"Therefore I must play the performing monkey," said Kieron calmly.

"I would not have described your role as such." Hobart tried to feign indignation, and failed. "Your task is to make sketches which will be invaluable when we come to decide upon the final composition."

"A monkey with a charcoal stick," conceded Kieron. "You yourself will execute the painting, Master Hobart.

I am simply to delay matters until you and Seigneur Fitzalan judge that the time is ripe."

"Not so, not so, not so!" protested Hobart. "You will execute the portrait."

"You would trust me with this matter?"

"Kieron, I would trust you with my life. . . . Besides, look at my hands, boy. Look at them."

Master Hobart held out his hands. Kieron looked. They were shaking badly. The veins stood out, the joints were swollen, the fingers were bent. Such hands would never draw a true circle again.

"Master Hobart, I am sorry. Truly, I am sorry."

"No need for sorrow, Kieron, my son. No need. I have you. Seigneur Fitzalan does not know that I have finished with painting."

"You have not finished with painting, Master."

"Hear me. Hear me. The portrait will be signed Hobart. It is the last time I shall put my signature. . . . But, when Seigneur Fitzalan has given his approval, I shall add to that signature. It shall read: Hobart app Kieron. Is that enough?"

Kieron was amazed to find himself weeping. "Master Hobart, you cannot do this thing."

"I can and will. Is it enough?"

"It is more than enough. Much more."

"This once, and this once only, I require you to call me Father. And I require you to paint Mistress Alyx in such a fashion that it will add stature to us both."

"Father, I will do my best," said Kieron.

"I am content. Your best is good enough. . . . Seigneur Fitzalan has undertaken to pay seven hundred and fifty schilling for a successful portrait."

"Seven hundred and fifty schilling!" It was the first time Kieron had ever heard Master Hobart talk of money. The sum mentioned was enormous. Kieron's own official allowance was ten schilling a year.

"Mark you, the fee also includes the time that must be spent and the trouble taken to produce the preliminary sketches which will, with Ludd's help, take up many of Mistress Alyx's waking hours during the next eight-week."

Kieron snorted. "More a fee for the diversion than for the portrait, I'll wager."

"My son, it is not for us to dissect Seigneur Fitzalan's generosity. Now, listen carefully. You have seen my hands. Also you must know by now that I paint horses less elegantly — shall we say — than I might. ... It is a strange thing, this matter of horses. But all artists have some weakness. No matter. I digress. ... The point is that you will execute the portrait. It will be a good one, that I already know. And in the matter of the signature, the world shall see that the master has been outstripped by the apprentice. But to return to the fee. Upon Seigneur Fitzalan's approval and payment, two hundred and fifty schilling shall be sent to Master Gerard, thus to recognise that the son of his flesh and the child of my spirit are formidably one person; two hundred and fifty schilling shall be held for you against your majority and the completion of your apprenticeship; and the remaining two hundred and fifty schilling I will keep, in fee for what I have taught you and to dispose of as I wish. ... Does this arrangement please you, Kieron?"

For a time, Kieron was at a loss for words. At length, he said: "Master Hobart, you destroy me with kindness. I accept your generosity in all except one thing. The signature."

"You have seen my hands. I will paint no more. It is true that I will attend to simple matters. My eye is good for design and composition. I can still produce schemes for good murals. But I will paint no more."

"I will not have it so!" shouted Kieron.

Hobart was amazed. "My son, these are facts."

"Sir, you will sign the canvas Hobart, or I will void my apprenticeship and sell refined flax seed oil for a living."

"But why? But why?" Hobart could not understand why Kieron could decline a sudden rise to fame.

Kieron could not find the right words. But the ones he

had to manage with seemed good enough. "Because, sir, I have the good fortune to serve and be instructed by a master painter. It is my pleasure to enjoy the privilege. I can say no more."

Hobart promptly had a fit of coughing to conceal his emotions. Kieron brought him a flask of usquebaugh.

When he went up to the castle on that first morning of his attendance upon Mistress Alyx, it was raining heavily. Which was a good thing in some respects. Kieron wished to give some thought to the problems involved, before he attempted to limn a horse in motion.

Mistress Alyx, dressed in a morning gown of blue linen, cut a trifle high above the ankle and a trifle low above the breast, received him in a long room whose walls were covered with shelves on which lay many books. Kieron had never seen so many books. He stared at them open-mouthed, a greedy look in his eyes.

Mistress Alyx, seated at a clavichord, stared at the damp young man with disdain.

"Well, boy, are you here to gawp at books or to begin making a likeness of me?"

"Your pardon, Mistress Alyx. Forgive me. I have never seen so many books." Kieron advanced awkwardly across a rich Persian carpet, leaving behind him the wet imprint of his boots.

"You drip more than a washerwoman, bumpkin. I am minded to have my father's men put you out."

"Then I shall drip even more, Mistress. It cannot have escaped your notice that the skies have opened."

"Do not exercise your simple wit, prentice. Recollect that you are dealing with a high-born person."

"Forgive me again, Mistress Alyx. I have yet to adjust to the importance of my task."

"Then commence your task, boy, and say no more."

"Yes, Mistress. Would you be gracious enough to remain still for a short time?" Kieron, not having been offered a chair, squatted on the carpet and pinned paper to his drawing board.

"If I choose to move, I shall move," retorted Alyx. "Your hair is too long and you stink somewhat. I do not think I can bear your presence with great patience."

Kieron bit his tongue and selected a piece of charcoal from his pouch. He began to sketch Mistress Alyx as he saw her.

"You are contracted to the slut Petrina, I understand."

"Yes, Mistress."

"She is quite pretty, but you are odious. Poor child. We women are rarely lucky in the men chosen for us."

"Yes, Mistress."

"Do not talk, bumpkin. Get on with your work."

Kieron's hand was shaking badly. The lines he described were terrible, and he knew that this first sketch could be nothing less than grotesque.

"Let me see what you have done. Though you are ill-dressed and your conversation deformed, and though you are the son of a peasant, you may yet have talent."

Mistress Alyx was enjoying herself. This one she would roast over a slow fire.

"Mistress, the sketch is but a trial," said Kieron desperately. "It is not worthy of your inspection."

"Nevertheless, I would see it." She rose from her seat at the clavichord, came to where Kieron sat and peered down at the sketch.

"Ludd have mercy! You draw like a dotard. Get from my presence, boy. I do not wish to see you again."

"Yes, Mistress Alyx. I am sorry." Kieron gathered up his papers and charcoal sticks and drawing board. It seemed to him that his best recourse was to leave the castle and quietly hang himself.

"Until tomorrow," added Mistress Alyx in silky tones. "Present yourself at this time tomorrow, boy. And pray for happier circumstances."

Kieron fled sweating. He did not hang himself. But when it was time to go to his bed, he was greatly troubled by nightmares.

7

THE FOLLOWING DAY it rained also. This time Kieron took precautions. He covered his head and shoulders with sackcloth and wrapped his drawing materials and a spare pair of boots in the same material. Then he trudged up to the castle. Before he was taken to Mistress Alyx, he begged leave to straighten his hair and change his boots.

She received him as before, seated at the clavichord in the long, book-lined room.

"So, boy, you keep time. That is something. And you contrive to appear less bedraggled. That, also, is something. Let us hope that this time you will not ruin good paper. . . . Well, don't stand there like a scarecrow. Find somewhere to sit, and begin to prove that my dear father is not recklessly throwing away many a good schilling."

Kieron felt the blood rush to his face. A volley of words struggled to burst from his throat, but he compressed his lips and stifled them. He stood rooted to the spot. There was no chair within reach, so he sat on the carpet.

"I hope your breeches are clean," said Alyx. "The carpet came from a far land, of which you are doubtless not aware, and cost more schilling than your poor talent is like to earn you in a lifetime."

"Mistress," he retorted softly, "my breeches are clean, and I am aware that the carpet is of Persian style. Whether it came from Persia, I know not; though I am told that the Flemish weavers now make carpets in the Persian style, which are less costly than the originals and, therefore, of some convenience to the nobility."

The carpet was Persian, as Kieron well knew. But

some retaliation seemed necessary, and he chose the first that came to mind.

"Impudent peasant!" stormed Alyx. "The carpet is truly Persian."

"Mistress Alyx, I am indeed a peasant, and I doubt not your word," said Kieron with every possible inference of doubting. "May I commence?" He felt better.

"Yes, stupid one. Scratch the paper if you must. But let your representation be better than that of yesterday, else I swear my father's bailiff shall kick you all the way from the castle to Master Hobart's hovel. The poor man must be in his dotage to have taken such a prentice as you."

"I may do him little credit," said Kieron, "but Master Hobart is the finest painter in the south country. The finished portrait will be to your liking, Mistress. That I can swear."

For some minutes there was silence. Kieron sketched, Alyx fidgeted, but not too much.

Kieron felt he could get the measure of this young lady. She must be vulnerable. She must be vulnerable, as all women were, to flattery. So, his hand being steady now, he was able to flatter her. He made her eyes larger and more beautiful than they were, he narrowed her waist, he gave fullness to her breasts, he made her hair cascade luxuriantly round her shoulders.

Presently, curiosity overcame her. "I would see your scribblings, boy."

Kieron stood up; but, one leg being stiff and numb from sitting cross-legged to support his drawing board, he promptly fell down.

Alyx laughed. "No doubt your legs give way with fear at my disapproval."

Kieron said nothing. He picked up the drawing, hobbled to the clavichord, and laid the paper before her.

She studied it. "My nose is not bent," she said, "and my ears are smaller. But you have improved somewhat since yesterday. Perhaps there is hope."

"Thank you, Mistress."

"I said perhaps," she warned. "Perhaps means only perhaps." She glanced at one of the leaded windows. "See. The rain has stopped. Now we shall ride."

Kieron was nonplussed. "Mistress, I do not ride. My commission is only to take your likeness in many attitudes and aspects."

"Your commission, boy, is to attend me. It is agreed that Master Hobart shall depict me on horseback. In order for you to make studies of horses, you must be familiar with them — and with me when I ride. Therefore you will ride also. Wait here while I change."

As Kieron waited, the books on the shelves became as magnets, drawing him. So many books! So many wonderful, glorious books. And they must be old, very old. The neddies, of necessity, permitted the use of printing machines — but only for the dissemination of approved sacred texts. Here were books that dealt not only with the works and life of Ned Ludd but also with all manner of recondite themes.

Mistress Alyx took much time to change into her riding apparel. While he was alone, Kieron began to examine the books. Many of them were immensely old, their bindings nibbled by mice, their papers brown and speckled with the ravages of time. There were works of biography — the lives of the seigneurs of Arundel, and many others — works of history, works concerning the skills of warfare, farming, hunting; works concerning voyages of discovery, the establishment of trade with far countries; works concerning the study of the stars. And there was one thin, incredibly tattered, incredibly ancient book about the development of infernal machines — including flying machines.

Kieron pored over it greedily. Some of the words were hard, some incomprehensible. Nevertheless, it began to yield information — about people with strange names, who had accomplished strange things, such as the

Brothers Montgolfier, Otto Lilienthal, Santos Dumont — until Mistress Alyx returned.

Guiltily, Kieron closed the book and pushed it back into its place on the shelves.

"Boy, did I give you permission to examine my father's books?"

"No, Mistress Alyx."

"Then do not presume. Come, we will ride."

"I cannot ride, Mistress." Kieron had never felt less like attempting to mount a horse.

"You will ride, boy. It is my wish." Alyx had the air of one anticipating much amusement.

The episode was doomed — as Mistress Alyx had intended. She had an old mare saddled for Kieron; so old and so gentle, she told him, that a child barely able to walk would be assured of a safe ride. For herself, Alyx chose a fine, spirited hunter.

Having had the grooms hoist Kieron more or less bodily into the saddle, Alyx led the way, allowing her horse to amble down the hill from the castle and among the cluster of houses that marked the growing township. Kieron followed as best he could, his teeth rattling somewhat in his head, and his bottom rising from the saddle and hitting it again somewhat heavily.

People looked up as Mistress Alyx rode by. Women curtsied, men touched their hats. They marvelled indeed to see that she was accompanied by Kieron the prentice boy, and were amused at his obvious discomfiture. Petrina saw him struggling anxiously to retain his seat, and could not repress a smile. Two or three idle apprentices made so bold as to cheer.

Once Arundel was behind, Alyx allowed her horse to canter. The open grazing land was still soggy from the rain, but the going was not too bad. Except for Kieron. Independent of anything he might do, the old mare seemed to take guidance from the hunter — or secretly from Mistress Alyx.

Soon Kieron had abandoned the reins and was hanging

on desperately to his poor animal by its mane. Inevitably, he fell off.

Mistress Alyx had chosen to ride by the bank of the river Arun, now swollen with the rains. It was a cunning choice; for when Kieron became unseated there was an even chance that he would fall on the river side.

Ludd was not with him, and he did. He fell into a large patch of mud, taking much of the fall upon his shoulder and the rest upon his backside as he rolled over. It was worse than a body slam at wrestling on the green.

Alyx laughed heartily. "So, prentice, your horsemanship is the equal of your limning. Mount again, boy. Do not look so dazed. I do not choose to wait here for ever."

Kieron mounted, somehow. Aching and bruised, he managed to get back on to the mare. He did not stay in the saddle for long. The next time, however, he had the good sense to fall not on the river side but on the pasture side. It hurt more, but there was no mud. He got to his feet, shaking and aching. Blindly, he tried to get back into the saddle.

"Enough, boy. You have so terrified my gentle mare that she will throw you as soon as she feels your weight. Follow me back to the castle. I will go slow. Lead her carefully. She is not accustomed to boors."

Alyx turned her horse round and, hardly glancing at Kieron, headed back through Arundel to the castle. Still showing extensive streaks of mud on his face and clothes, and visibly shaken, Kieron followed her, casting many nervous glances backwards at the docile mare he was leading.

The townsfolk who were about surveyed the spectacle and took care not to let Mistress Alyx see their amusement. However, they also took care that Kieron-head-in-the-air, whose muddy face was now downcast, should see. Worst of all, Petrina, having made purchases at the bakery, was now returning home with a basketful of fresh bread. At first, when she saw Kieron, her expression was one of horror; then slowly it changed, and she could not repress a smile. The smile hurt him as if it had been a blow.

At the castle, solemn-faced grooms relieved him of the mare. A lackey, commanded by Alyx, went through the motions of cleaning him up a little, with obvious distaste for the task. Kieron's clothes were of good, honest doeskin and wool. The lackey wore linen and velvet. Kieron thought it would be a heaven-sent convenience if he were suddenly to die.

Unfortunately, Ludd was not merciful. He remained alive. Mistress Alyx, with no expression at all on her face, directed him to attend her in the library. He followed submissively, resolving to gather up his materials and take leave of her as soon as possible.

His sketch and drawing board were on the Persian carpet where he had left them: Alyx seemed not to notice their existence. She went straight to the clavichord; and her riding boots, still wet and bearing traces of mud, left their imprint upon Kieron's sketch as she walked over it.

Suddenly he knew that he had reached the limits of endurance. To take more humiliation from this spoilt girl would be to accept more than his manhood could permit.

"Enough, bitch!" he cried. "I have had more than enough of you!"

Alyx turned to him, affecting surprise, indignation. Cool and controlled indignation. "Boy, you have exceeded yourself. You have used a certain word in my presence and directed at my person. For that I will have you whipped from the castle. Your apprenticeship will be dissolved and you will be sent forth to live as best you may on nuts in the woods."

"Not before I have taught you a lesson," retorted Kieron icily. "Mistress, I am a freeborn man and I have dignity. Your blood may be noble, but your manners are exceedingly crude."

And with that, he lifted her bodily, sat upon the stool

by the clavichord and proceeded to spank her bottom with much vigour and enthusiasm.

Alyx screamed. Kieron enjoyed her screaming mightily. He was enjoying it so much that he was unaware of the doors of the library bursting open as servants rushed in. He was aware of nothing but the exquisite pleasure of spanking this spoilt child who presumed to be a woman. He was aware of nothing else until hands seized him and he was struck on the head and sank into oblivion.

8

HE AWOKE TO find himself in what seemed to be the castle donjon. He awoke because a pailful of cold water had been hurled at his face. He awoke to find himself hanging by his hands from manacles fastened into the stone wall. He awoke to find that his wrists ached, his arms ached, his shoulders ached, his head ached. He awoke to find that Seigneur Fitzalan, seated on a chair, was facing him. By Seigneur Fitzalan's side stood the castle gaoler. Behind his chair stood the Mistress Alyx.

They will kill me, thought Kieron hazily. I care not. Better to die like a man than live like a sheep.

"So, prentice, you are kind enough to rejoin us." Seigneur Fitzalan's voice was pleasant, gentle, even. But his countenance was stern. Kieron saw no mercy in it.

"Forgive me, Seigneur," said Kieron with accidental humour, "I was not conscious of your presence."

"Ha!" Seigneur Fitzalan permitted himself a thin smile. "I will remember the jest . . . Well, boy, you struck the Mistress Alyx, repeatedly, in a place to which no gentleman cares to refer. Before I determine your fate, I would have you know that this is a precedent. Derive some satisfaction from it, if you may. Previous to your assault, no man — not even I — had ever laid hand upon my daughter in anger. What, then have you to say?"

"Nothing, Seigneur," said Kieron after a moment or two of reflection. It would be stupid to plead for mercy. It would be stupid to try to explain the provocation.

"So, boy, you are fairly condemned?"

"I struck Mistress Alyx, Seigneur. I intended no permanent damage. That is all." He looked vaguely at Alyx. She was no longer the imperious young lady. She seemed white-faced, unhappy. Well, thought Kieron, let my death lie on her conscience for ever.

"That is all?" thundered Fitzalan. "That is all?"

"Seigneur," said the goaler, "allow me to encourage him."

"Be silent, fellow," snapped Fitzalan irritably. "A knock on the head and his present situation ought to be sufficiently encouraging for the time being . . . Well, prentice, you have spoken. You have nothing further to add?"

Kieron thought for a moment. There was much that could be added, of course, but best keep it to essentials.

"I pray that my actions will not reflect upon Master Hobart, who is a kindly man and a great painter, and responsible for no actions but his own. I pray also that my parents be held free from blame. It was simply their misfortune to beget me. Already, they have their punishment."

Seigneur Fitzalan made rumbling noises in his throat. His moustache quivered. Mistress Alyx leaned forward and, looking at Kieron, began to stroke her father's long silver hair.

"As to your punishment, prentice, I have given some thought to it. At first, I was minded to have your head struck off, as an example to all upstarts and mischiefmakers, of which there are always a few in any domain. Then, since such a punishment was somewhat final and likely to be forgotten by many in a twelve-month, I was inclined to clemency, striking off only the offending hand and blinding the offending eyes."

Kieron shuddered. Death was preferable to clemency.

"However," continued Seigneur Fitzalan, "my daughter Alyx, who is not without a mind of her own, suggested a more ingenious punishment."

Kieron's mouth ran dry. The horrors already mentioned

seemed bad enough. But, evidently, they were not sufficient to give Mistress Alyx the satisfaction she required.

"So, prentice, you will endure the punishment that Mistress Alyx has recommended, since she is the offended party."

"Seigneur," said Kieron quickly, "I accept death by decapitaton. It is just."

"Do you, now? The choice lies not in your province, boy. Think yourself fortunate."

Kieron did not think himself fortunate. The axe was quick, whereas whatever Mistress Alyx had devised was likely to be slow.

"I sentence you," said Seigneur Fitzalan, smiling faintly, "to attend Mistress Alyx upon her request, to execute such drawings as are necessary, and never again to raise your hand towards her in anger, lest mine be raised fearfully against you . . . You are lucky, boy, that my daughter enjoys peculiar whims and also has womanly methods of twisting my resolution. Well, what say you?"

Kieron's mouth opened and closed, but no words would come.

"Loose him, father. The boy has suffered enough." Alyx gazed compassionately at Kieron. It was the first time she had spoken.

Fitzalan cast a despairing glance at ceiling. "When will I ever understand the ways of a woman?" Then he signalled to the gaoler, and Kieron was released from the manacles.

He found his tongue. "I thank you, Seigneur, for the mercy you have shown."

Fitzalan laughed. "Mercy, by Ludd! Speak to me of mercy when Mistress Alyx has taken her vengeance. Now get from this place and pray somewhat."

9

THE FOLLOWING DAY, Kieron presented himself at the castle as usual; but Mistress Alyx chose not to receive him. He returned to Hobart's house dejected, convinced that Alyx had had time for reflection and that the commission was lost, seven hundred and fifty schilling and all. He supposed he ought to count himself lucky that he got out of the affair as lightly as he did. But he was truly mortified. He was mortified because he feared that his conduct might reflect upon Master Hobart, and that the old man might lose other commissions also.

He had related the entire story as accurately as he could, adding nothing, omitting nothing. He had expected that Hobart would be dismayed and also disgusted with him, would wish to beat him certainly, and quite likely would desire to end the apprenticeship.

He was right in that Hobart was dismayed. He was wrong in that Hobart would be disgusted.

"My son, I see that Mistress Alyx used you cruelly. Forgive me. I know that she is a wilful woman. I did not know that she would abuse her position. It matters not if we are out of favour at the castle. I liked this commission but little, anyway. What matters most is that you survived the incident." He tried to laugh, but wound up with a fit of coughing that needed to be settled by usquebaugh. "In any case, we have the refined flax seed oil, for which the demand will be prodigious."

Kieron was amazed. "You are not angry?"

"Yes, I am angry that talent should be impeded by temperament. What is Alyx Fitzalan? Nothing but the

55

daughter of Seigneur Fitzalan. That is her sole significance. But you, Kieron, are an artist and quite possibly
a man of genius. It is unfortunate that you beat her —
though I rejoice in the thought, having had some temptation myself — yet it is not disastrous. Fitzalan was
wise enough not to pursue the matter. We shall live."

"Sir, I am grateful."

"Say no more, Kieron. Tomorrow we will fish for
trout."

But, on the following day a lackey brought a summons.
The Mistress Alyx Fitzalan desired that Kieron, apprentice of Hobart, attend her with his drawing materials.

"You will not go," said Hobart. "I will plead illness."

"Sir, I must go," said Kieron. "It is part of the
sentence."

As before, Alyx was seated at the clavichord, waiting
for him. A book rested on the music machine. Kieron
recognised it.

"Good morning, Master Kieron." He was taken aback
at her civility. Besides, he was not a master, he was only
an apprentice.

"Good morning, Mistress Alyx."

She stood up and held out the book.

"You were interested in this volume, I recall. It is
yours."

Kieron was shaken. "Mistress Alyx, you are most kind."
He took the book, fingered it lovingly. "You are too
kind. I — " He stopped.

Alyx smiled. "Let us forget the past, Kieron. How
would you like me to pose?"

"As you will, Mistress. As you will. I can take many
sketches and compound them into something from which
Master Hobart will discern the necessary form."

"Kieron?"

"Mistress Alyx?"

"Call me Alyx."

He was shaken even more. "Yes — Alyx."

"Kieron, no man ever before beat me."

"I am sorry, Mistress — I am sorry, Alyx. I thought you commanded me to forget the —"

"Kieron?"

"Mistress — I mean Alyx?"

She rose from the clavichord and came close to him. Her gown rustled, and there was a fragrance about her, a redness in her cheeks, a softness in her eyes. She did not now look at all like the ice-cold girl who had goaded him beyond endurance. "I treated you ill, and I am sorry. Yesterday, I cried into the night because I had been cruel and stupid, and I thought you would hate me. Do you hate me? If so, I must learn to bear it."

Kieron knew not what to say or do. For reasons he could not understand, his heart seemed to be exploding in his chest. There was sweat on his forehead and a fire in his limbs. At length he found his tongue.

"Mistress, I do not hate you. Truly, I do not. Something has happened that . . . Perhaps my mind is sick."

She smiled. "You forget. Say Alyx. My name is Alyx. You shall use it always when we are alone."

"Alyx," he said idiotically. "Alyx." He could think of nothing else to say. The word seemed both familiar and strange, a magic word. An incantation.

"Your mind is not sick, Kieron. At least, no more than mine . . . We are friends, now?"

"We are friends." Kieron was trembling. He seemed to be standing outside himself. He seemed to be listening to the voice of a stranger . . . Why did she stand so close? Why was there a roaring in his head?

"We are close friends?"

"If it is your wish."

"Is it not yours?"

"Alyx, I — I . . ." There was nothing to say. Nothing that made sense.

"Kiss me, Kieron. Your lips on mine." The book dropped from Kieron's hand. He did not notice. Neither of them noticed.

57

"Kiss me," she whispered. It was a whisper that drove all rational thought from Kieron's mind.

He held her in his arms. He felt the life in her. He felt her breasts against him, the liquid warmth of her belly. He felt her lips upon his.

This was like to earn him the donjon, the lash, the irons, the rack, all manner of tortures. He did not care. The taste of Alyx Fitzalan's lips, the touch of her body — he did not care.

Presently, they stood back from each other.

"No man ever beat me before. No man ever held me so before. No man ever kissed me so before." Alyx seemed happy, even complacent. "I love you, Kieron."

"I am terrified of love," said Kieron. "It is a destroyer. But I love you also. I thought I hated you, but the hatred was a form of love."

Alyx frowned as reality came back to her. "It is but a short-lived bloom, Kieron. Let us enjoy it while we may. The child Petrina is your destiny. Talbot of Chichester —a pale, sad thing — is mine . . . Does Petrina kiss as I do?"

"Alyx, I know not, I do not — I have not . . ." He floundered.

"Hush, dear one. You gave me my answer . . . Until this time, you were but a prentice painter bullied by a thoughtless minx, taking advantage of her father's power. But love is dangerous, Kieron. It makes us equal in each other's sight; but in the eyes of the world the gulf between us is wide. Talbot and Petrina, and the customs of our people, hover about us like ghosts. We must be very careful, otherwise we shall be destroyed."

Kieron managed to smile. "I will be careful, Alyx, if only because I must. I am afraid for both of us."

She took his hand. "Be not too much afraid. If we keep our heads, all will be well." She laughed. "I surmise my father required Master Hobart to keep me distracted for at least a two-month. Is that not so? And you were to be the sacrificial lamb."

Kieron shrugged. "It is so, Alyx. Indeed, it is so."

"Well, then," she said gaily, "who will protest if we stretch the two-month into a three-month? Not my father, not Master Hobart. Each would be delighted at the success of the stratagem. So, in public, I will be the haughty Alyx, whose aim is to humiliate you. And you will contrive to play the poor prentice who bears what he must for the sake of his master and his art and for the sake of his future. Can you bear this device?"

"I can bear it."

"Good. Today, you will make sketches; but, tomorrow, we will ride again. Doubtless, you will fall off. The people will learn of it and be satisfied. Kieron-head-in-the-air — yes, I know what they call you — will be humiliated once more. Can you bear it?"

"I can bear deception only for the sake of truth."

"Well spoken, my love." She came close and kissed him. "When we are alone — truly alone — you shall command me. I will kiss your feet, if it is your pleasure. I will stroke your hair and hold your body close to mine and rejoice in your touch."

"Alyx, do not make me cry."

"The tears will come later, Kieron — when I am taken to Talbot's bed, and Petrina comes to yours. How shall either of us bear it then?"

He held her tight. "I do not know. I know only that we have a little time. For that I am grateful."

"A little time," sighed Alyx. "Only a little time. So sad . . . I want to learn about you. I want to learn as much as I can. Do you truly want to be a painter like Master Hobart? Or is there something else."

"Most of all," said Kieron, caressing her, "I want to fly. I want to conquer the air as the First Men and the Second Men did. I want to feel close to the stars."

"Kieron-head-in-the-air," she murmured, "I love you. You are nothing but a fantasist, a cloud walker."

10

Brother Sebastian gazed at Kieron, lying on his day-bed, without any animosity or any attempt to inspire fear. Brother Sebastian, a pleasant-looking man of thirty years or so, concealed his ambition, his desire for power, beneath a benign exterior. He rarely bullied. He preferred to look sorrowful. People did not like to see Brother Sebastian unhappy.

Kieron's broken leg twitched abominably. It had been set by Seigneur Fitzalan's own surgeon. Nevertheless, Kieron remained convinced that the fellow knew little of his art. Already, when he stretched and measured his limbs, Kieron seemed to detect that the good leg was significantly longer. He would hate to exchange his present title for Kieron-game-leg. Besides, who would condescend to wrestle with a cripple?

Brother Sebastian was in a quandary. At the insistence of Mistress Alyx, Kieron had been removed temporarily from Hobart's house and given a room at the castle. Alyx had roundly condemned Kieron to her father, for indulging in childish pranks, and had implied that Kieron had broken his leg almost deliberately in order to avoid making the sketches and rough compositions that were necessary for the commissioned painting. Why, therefore, let the prentice have an easy time of it? Better, surely, to bring him to the castle so that he could continue his work without delay. That would teach him that he could not evade important affairs merely by breaking a leg.

Seigneur Fitzalan gave his daughter a curious look. He was an intelligent man. Intelligent enough to realise there were certain things it were better not to know. Besides, the boy was useful. Alyx had been relatively docile since she had had the prentice on whom to vent her feelings. So Kieron had been given a room in the castle while his leg mended.

Thus Brother Sebastian's quandary. Kieron, though a commoner, was now a person of some importance — temporarily, at least.

"Tell me, brother, how came you to break the limb?" This was a rhetorical question, because everyone in the seigneurie knew how Kieron had broken his leg.

"Brother Sebastian, I was but flying a kite," said Kieron carefully.

"A kite? You were flying a kite. I have been misinformed, it seems. I had heard that you were flying *in* a kite."

Kieron thought for a moment or two. Brother Sebastian had flung back his cowl. His head was clean-shaven; his face, totally visible, seemed totally innocent.

"It is true, brother," amended Kieron. "I was flying in a kite."

"It must have been an exceptionally large kite."

"It was, Brother Sebastian. It was a very large kite. I designed it."

"And who aided you in this project, Kieron?"

Kieron thought carefully. If he admitted that Aylwin had obtained the sail canvas, that they had both cut the willow rods and that Sholto, the smith, had been persuaded to make fastenings for the harness, it could seem like conspiracy.

"No one, Brother Sebastian. It is true I coaxed the miller's prentice to hold the rope. He is but a stupid fellow and fit for nothing but the grinding of corn. However, dull though he is, it pleased me to make use of him. I little recked that he would take panic when I rose into the air."

The neddy stroked his chin thoughtfully. "That must indeed have been a sight."

"Indeed it must, brother," said Kieron with unguarded enthusiasm. "There was a steady and strong offshore breeze, and I rose up from the beach, my legs dancing and seeking footholds where there were none. It was a wonderful feeling. I rose more than ten times the height of a man before the loop of cord was jerked from its hook."

"You were lucky, Kieron, that the sea broke your fall."

"That is why I waited for an offshore wind," explained Kieron. "That is why I chose to experiment on the beach."

"Experiment?" Brother Sebastian raised his eyebrows. Experiment was a dangerous word. It smelled of fire.

"Experiment in the sense of finding out how to handle the kite," amended Kieron hastily. "Nothing more."

Brother Sebastian stroked his chin slowly. At length, he said: "The kite was made of sail-cloth and willow wands."

"Yes, brother."

"And the harness as you call it had metal fastenings which could only have been fashioned by the smith."

"Yes, brother."

"It was a very ambitious kite, Kieron."

"Yes, Brother Sebastian. It was a very ambitious kite."

"And you designed it alone?"

"I designed it alone."

"Sholto did not know your purpose?"

"No, brother."

"And the boy Aylwin helped you only by anchoring the cord and by moving as directed?"

"Yes, brother."

"I am told you instructed him in the use of a pulley, by which means he could control the kite without great exertion to himself."

"You are well informed."

"Yes, Kieron. I am well informed."

"The pulley. It is a very simple principle."

"Simple principles can be dangerous, Kieron. You have been instructed in the Holy Scripture, have you not?"

"Yes, brother."

"Men have burned for simple principles, Kieron. Remember that."

Kieron wanted to rise from his bed and strangle this dull-witted neddy. But he had enough wit to say docilely: "Yes, Brother Sebastian."

"I have heard," went on the neddy, "that folk call you Kieron-head-in-the-air. Why should they call you that?"

Kieron thought quickly, gave a shrug, and laughed. "Since I fell from Mistress Alyx Fitzalan's mare, they also call me Kieron-arse-in-the-muck. People amuse themselves as they wish." It seemed as good a time as any to remind Brother Sebastian that Kieron was permitted to ride with Seigneur Fitzalan's daughter.

The neddy was not to be distracted. "You do not know why they call you Kieron-head-in-the-air?"

"Brother, perhaps it is because I often look at the sky. The sky is a wonderful place. It is ever-changing. Its moods are always different."

"You are fascinated by the sky?"

"Yes, Brother Sebastian, I am fascinated by the sky."

"And you wish to voyage through it?"

Now, there was a dangerous question. Kieron was immediately alert to its implications.

"The sky, the firmament, is beautiful," he said carefully. "The artist in me is profoundly moved by its aspects, and by the subtle changes it undergoes throughout the seasons... To the greater glory of Ludd."

Brother Sebastian crossed himself. "To the greater glory of Ludd," he echoed automatically. After a reverent pause, he continued: "But do you wish to voyage through it?"

Kieron's leg was hurting, and sweat was forming on his forehead, and he did not know how long he could endure the damnable persistence of the neddy.

"I can admire the freedom of the bird without wishing to sprout feathers. I am a man, Brother Sebastian, accepting the freedom and the limitations of men. I rejoice in my human condition."

"But, Kieron, my brother, do you wish to fly?"

"Brother Sebastian, I do not wish to be a bird."

Brother Sebastian sighed, and looked unhappy. "Your answers are less than direct."

"I am sorry, brother. I thought my answers were accurate and truthful. This accursed leg gives me pain. Perhaps I do not think too clearly."

"Perhaps so. I shall report our conversation to Holy Church, Kieron. Others, more competent than I, will consider it."

"That is well, Brother Sebastian," said Kieron, thinking it was far from well. "Perhaps my childish adventure was ill-timed."

"Kites are for children only, Kieron. Remember that. You are almost a man."

"I will remember it."

"Further, a kite is but a toy. But if a man should choose to ride a kite, it could be interpreted as a machine."

"I will remember that also."

"I shall pray for you," said Brother Sebastian. "You have a great future. Master Hobart tells me that you are gifted in your craft. Do not spoil that future, Kieron. Good painters are rare. Evil men are with us always."

"I will remember your words, Brother Sebastian, and I shall dwell upon your wisdom."

"Ludd be with you, my brother."

"And with you also."

"Farewell, then." Brother Sebastian departed. Hardly had he gone, when Alyx came into the room.

"How went your discussion with Brother Sebastian?"

"He is a fool."

"My love, I know that. But was he satisfied?"

"I don't know."

"You should know. Why don't you know?"

"Because I too am a fool," said Kieron irritably, "and my leg twitches . . ." Then he smiled, and added: "And it is a fine day, and I would be out walking in the woods with you."

"This will teach you to try to walk upon air, when we have so little time." She shuddered. "You could have been killed. Promise me to be more careful, Kieron."

He glanced at his leg. "I can hardly be but careful, Alyx."

"Not now, dolt. In the future, as you well know."

"I will be careful until you are carried off to Talbot's bed," he promised rightly. "Then I will construct a kite that shall raise me high above your father's castle. Then I will leap from it and dash myself to death before his eyes."

Alyx pouted. "I wish Talbot would die. I truly do. And I wish the plague or somesuch would carry off that dreadful Petrina, with her peasant breasts and a bottom like a cow's rump. Ludd forgive me, I pray for these things."

"Petrina does not have a bottom like a cow's rump."

"She does so. I have studied her."

He laughed. "Ah, you have studied her, Green Eyes."

"I hate you! I hate you."

"Come, let me sketch you while the fire still consumes you. I must earn my keep lest Seigneur Fitzalan and Master Hobart begin to imagine the absurdity that is the truth."

"Peasant!" she stormed.

"Yes, I am a peasant," he replied tranquilly. "Be mindful that the gulf between us is great — with or without Talbot and Petrina."

"I love you, and I would die for you. Is that not enough?"

"It is too much. I love you, as you know, Alyx, and we must both live in a world where such love is an affront to the minds of men ... Besides, I have a destiny to fulfil."

"I would not stop you painting."

"You would stop me flying."

She looked at him in amazement. "Flying! Kieron, my

love. You are mad. Men do not fly. Men will not fly."

"Yes, I am mad — and I will fly. I will construct a machine that —"

"Do not speak of machines! Or, if you must, to me only. Machines are evil. That is the word of the Divine Boy, that is the teaching of Holy Church, that is what all men know."

"And yet," said Kieron, "it is not true. Machines cannot be evil. Evil lies only with the human spirit . . . I will fly, I swear it. I will fly for the good of men. By the spirits of the Brothers Montgolfier, of Otto Lilienthal, of the great Santos Dumont, and of the Brothers Wright, I so swear."

"Who are these creatures?"

"Nothing but ghosts. Great and friendly ghosts. Men who lived centuries ago upon earth and raised their eyes unto the stars . . . I read of them in the book you gave me."

"I had done better to burn it. My father does not read, and therefore cannot have known that his library contained heresy."

"Had you burned it, Alyx, I still would have lifted my eyes unto the stars. It is not in the nature of man to remain earthbound . . . Come, kiss me. Then I will try to be of some credit to Master Hobart."

II

THE DAYS PASSED quickly. Kieron's leg mended and was not noticeably shorter. Spring deepened into summer — and brought a bloom to Mistress Alyx's face that did not pass unnoticed. She taught Kieron to ride — or, at least, not to fall off a horse when it was in motion. He made studies of horses. Horses grazing, horses ambling, galloping, jumping. The first time Alyx took her mount over a seven-bar gate for him, he was too terrified to put charcoal to paper.

"My love, never again! Don't do it. You are like to break your neck."

"Poof! Thus speaks the cloud walker, who rose ten times the height of a man and fell into the sea." And, to emphasise her point, she put her horse to the gate again; and rose, chestnut hair streaming in the sunlight, to ride like a goddess between sky and earth in a moment of infinite beauty.

Kieron worked like a demon, like one possessed. He made a hundred sketches and discarded ninety. This portrait of Alyx Fitzalan would be his sole claim to greatness as an artist. He knew it would be good, because it would be compounded of love, of beauty, of youth, and of joy in life.

Master Hobart coughed much and complained little. He complained little because Kieron had ceased to complain at all.

Hobart gazed at the sketches he brought back, and was filled with wonder. The boy had achieved rapport with his subject. There was elegance in his work and, yes, greatness.

Hobart reached for the usquebaugh or the eau de vie and contemplated this greatness. Escapades with kites mattered little — indeed, were irrelevant — against such purity of line, such mastery of motion.

Soon, Kieron would begin to paint. Not at the castle, but in Hobart's studio. And the painting would be a masterpiece, signed Hobart. And when is was acclaimed a masterpiece, Hobart would add: app Kieron. Thus would his life's work be completed. Thus would Kieron be set upon the path to fame.

Kieron executed the painting in one day only. One day being a full twenty-four hours. During that time, he did not speak. He did not recognise Hobart. The old man hovered about the canvas, wringing his hands, and Kieron did not know him. The Widow Thatcher brought food. Kieron stared at her, uncomprehending, and the food was left untouched. As darkness fell, Hobart brought lamps, many lamps, and squandered whale oil prodigiously. Kieron muttered to himself at the change of light, but did not know what brought it about.

Once he fell to the floor, and was conscious of someone forcing a fluid that burned between his lips. He got up, and went back to the canvas. The rider was finished; but the fetlocks of the leaping horse were wrong. He scraped them away from the canvas and started again.

Now, what of that damned tail? And the nostrils? And, Ludd have mercy, the mane? And now the eyes were wrong. The creature should have great, proud eyes as it supported its glorious rider in that impossible leap. He looked at Alyx once more. Purgatory and damnation! The hair was wrong. That long, beautiful hair should flow with movement, be alive in this instant with a life of its own.

Master Hobart tended the oil lamps and drank usquebaugh and muttered plaintively to himself and gazed with awe at the young man who seemed to be engaged in a life or death battle with brushes and pigments as his weapons.

Who was the enemy? Hobart asked himself blearily, drunk with spirits and fatigue. Who was the enemy against which Kieron waged so ferocious a battle? It came to him that the enemy was time. Kieron was not only trying to paint a great portrait, he was challenging the Adversary. He was the Life Force incarnate; and every brush stroke was a sword thrust. He was declaring his bid for immortality.

The picture was finished shortly after daybreak. Hobart, who had dozed intermittently, drew back the curtains from the window but left the oil-lamps burning.

Kieron stood in front of the canvas. Brushes and palette had dropped from his exhausted hands.

Hobart gazed at the portrait and wept, knowing that he was in the presence of greatness.

Kieron looked at him, pale, drawn, red-eyed. "I have done my best, Master Hobart. What say you?"

"My son, my son!" the old man was beside himself. "You have joined the ranks of the immortals. I am a fool. I presumed to teach you. But now that it is too late, I know how much I had to learn."

"If you love me," said Kieron, "you will sign it Hobart. You will add nothing."

"Kieron, I am not worthy."

"The style is yours. Had you been younger, the brush strokes would have been yours."

"The brush strokes could never have been mine."

"They are yours, because I was an extension of your will." Kieron put his foot upon the fallen brushes. "Sir, I will not paint like this again."

"But why? Why, Kieron? You are a great artist. If you paint in this manner at the beginning of your career, who knows what we may see?"

"I will not paint like this again," repeated Kieron. "It was a work of love — doubly so." He laughed. "I may paint to live — though the work will be no more than adequate — if such is necessary. But I shall live to fly. That is my true destiny."

Hobart could say nothing. The picture was magnificent. But the poor boy was clearly out of his mind.

69

12

Seigneur Fitzalan was pleased with the painting. He did not know that Kieron had executed every brush stroke, though he surmised that much of the fine work had been carried out by the prentice. Master Hobart's shaking had become more noticeable; and it was plain even to Fitzalan that the old painter's useful days were numbered. Fortunate indeed that the prentice showed signs of surpassing his master. There would be work enough for him in the years to come. Fitzalan liked to be surrounded by beautiful things — paintings he merely glanced at, books he did not read. A man's greatness was reflected in his deeds or his possessions. Time had not granted Seigneur Fitzalan the opportunity to perform great deeds, but it had allowed him to acquire many fine works of art from goldsmiths, silversmiths, armourers, scribes, painters. He would be remembered for his taste, if for nothing else.

The painting was to be called: *Mistress Fitzalan's Leap*. The signature was simply: Hobart.

But Alyx knew how the picture had been finished, and she wept somewhat that Kieron's name did not rest upon this painting that would hold the glow of her youth for ever. She wept also because of the grace and artistry she discerned, knowing that it was truly a work of love. And she wept because the dream-days were over. Henceforth, she would have to meet Kieron — if she met him at all — by 'accident' in some lonely or clandestine place. Soon, even that would not be possible because the wedding with Talbot was less than a month away.

Seigneur Fitzalan sent his bailiff with a chamois leather bag containing seven hundred and fifty silver schilling to the house of Hobart. The bailiff also conveyed Fitzalan's desire that Kieron should attend him. Hobart was apprehensive, recollecting the last interview Kieron had had with Seigneur Fitzalan. But Kieron did not seem perturbed. He put on his best leather and linen and followed the bailiff.

Seigneur Fitzalan received him in a room that Kieron had not seen before; a room that contained many weapons, a desk, a table, two chairs, a bearskin rug and little else.

Seigneur Fitzalan was seated at the desk, toying with a fine hunting knife.

"Well, prentice, are you satisfied with *Mistress Fitzalan's Leap*?" The tone was even, but the voice was ominous.

"Seigneur, I — I —" Kieron floundered, suddenly thinking of a hundred things that could be wrong with the canvas. "It is as good, I think, as Master Hobart has ever done."

Fitzalan gave him a faint smile. "Ay, boy, that may be fairly said ... Since our last meeting, I have had reports of you. Both good and ill. Which would you hear first?"

Kieron began to sweat a little, but his wit did not desert him. "The ill, Seigneur. Then I may console myself with the good."

"The ill it is, then. Holy Church is interested in you, Kieron. I am told that you constructed a machine."

"Seigneur, I did but fashion a large kite that —"

"Enough, I know the details. Holy Church ruled long ago that a kite is but a toy. However, if such a toy be used to elevate a man unnaturally from the earth, it becomes a machine. You know the history of our race. Machines have twice destroyed the greatness of man. The wisdom of the Divine Boy is apparent. Men can only survive if they reject the temptation of machines. Is this not so?"

Kieron swallowed. "Seigneur, I must bow to the wisdom of Holy Church."

"That you must, boy. Machines smell of burning. Have you ever seen a man burn, Kieron?"

"No, Seigneur."

"I have," said Fitzalan tranquilly. "Holy Church is more powerful than all the lords of this island, and rightly so. For Holy Church guides us in the way we must live. I have seen a farmer burn for constructing a reaping machine. I have seen a smith burn for fashioning an engine driven by steam. I have seen a noble man burn for meddling with electrics and creating a light that was not born of fire. I have seen a poor washerwoman burn for devising a machine that would spin the water out of the clothes she washed. The stench of burnt flesh is not like the smell of roast pork, prentice. I make myself clear?"

"Seigneur, you make yourself excellently clear."

"Then, Kieron, let there be no more meddling with machines. I have writ to Holy Church that you are aware of your folly. This time, my protection holds. Do not think it will hold a second time."

"Seigneur, I am grateful."

"So you should be. But I am grateful also. *Mistress Fitzalan's Leap* is a good painting. Further, the conditions I sought from your master were met in full — with a bonus."

"I am happy, sir."

"Do not be. The bonus gives me cause for unrest. I required the Mistress Alyx's spare time to be engaged for a two-month. You, sir, engaged it for a three-month."

"There was the matter of my broken leg," Kieron floundered. "It took time to mend."

Seigneur Fitzalan lifted the hunting knife with which he had been playing and pointed it at Kieron. "My daughter, Alyx, was happy for a time. Now she weeps. Can you explain that?"

"Seigneur, I am at a loss."

Fitzalan laughed, grimly. "So, prentice, am I ... With women, it is always the unexpected that a man should anticipate. Mistress Alyx spoke well of you — not too well, but well enough. She can be careful of her tongue, that one, when it suits her ... Yet, now she weeps. She will wed with Talbot in a month. And yet, she weeps. Amazing, is it not?"

"Yes, Seigneur, it is amazing." Kieron dreaded the way the conversation was turning.

"Know this, then. There are things better unsaid; for if said, they must be admitted or denied. And in certain matters, either course leads to danger. Now, boy, do not think to be clever, but tell me if your mind truly grasps that which I have left unsaid."

Kieron swallowed, his eyes upon the hunting knife, which seemed to be pointing at his heart. "Sir, I understand you."

"So. I believe you." Seigneur Fitzalan put the hunting knife down. He took up a small chamois sack and rattled its contents. "The horse does not shame me, and I know that Master Hobart has no liking for horses. Also the rider is shown to be not without grace and distinction. At your art, boy, you may flourish. See that you flourish in nought else." He threw the small sack to Kieron. "These fifty schilling recognise that you have worked well under some difficulty. There are other gifts I could bestow for services that were not required. Be thankful that I do not."

"Yes, Seigneur."

"Go, then. And recollect that tears dry soon if more are not provoked."

"Yes, Seigneur." Feeling the sweat lie cold upon his forehead, Kieron left the chamber.

13

THERE WAS NO longer any need for Kieron to visit the castle daily, and he did not. The warning given him by Seigneur Fitzalan had been clear enough. Besides, surely it was in Alyx's own interest that she and Kieron did not see each other again? As Fitzalan had said, tears dry soon if more are not provoked.

And yet it was hard, very hard, to face the whole of life without holding Alyx in his arms again. But he would love Petrina. It would not be difficult to love Petrina. She would lie by his side through ten thousand nights, and bear his children, and whiten and weaken as he whitened and weakened. Age might cool the passions of youth, but it could only add to the sharing of things known and loved.

Each man has but a single lifetime, thought Kieron. We are here but for a moment in history. There is so little time. So little time to lift man from the face of the earth and make him lord of the sky once more.

Master Hobart was more than content with *Mistress Fitzalan's Leap*. Much more than content. He was proud that his spiritual son had carried the day in such triumph. Contractually, Kieron's apprenticeship had several months to run; but Hobart knew that he no longer gave bed and food to an apprentice. He knew that he was privileged to enjoy the society of a genius. A genius who had insisted that his first great work be signed Hobart. So Hobart did not exercise the rights of a master. He was content to be a proud and a spiritual father. Which meant that Kieron now enjoyed absolute freedom. And this, in turn, meant that Hobart was prey to exquisite anxieties.

Kieron now possessed fifty schilling to do with as he wished. A veritable fortune. More money than he had ever handled in his seventeen years. How to use it? There were problems. Twenty schillings for Aylwin, who had served him well in the matter of the man-lifting kite. Twenty schilling would buy much canvas and pigment and flax seed oil for Aylwin. Add to this Kieron's instruction, and Aylwin would be well repaid for his friendship. He would become a master painter as well as a master miller. Aylwin would rejoice in, at least, a partial freedom from his destiny.

The remaining thirty schilling ... Kieron had read the book given him by Alyx. He had read it many times. The conquest of the air had been carried out in steps. He would retrace those steps. And the next step was a hot-air balloon, such as had been fashioned by Joseph and Etienne Montgolfier many centuries ago.

For this, Kieron required much linen, and much paper to line the balloon that would be made of linen. Also, he required a small charcoal brazier. Also, he required again the help of Aylwin.

Mistress Alyx did not subscribe to the philosophy that tears dry soon if more are not provoked. Discreetly, she sent messages to Kieron. He did not dare reply. Then she took to riding daily through Arundel, pausing a while in front of Master Hobart's house. Kieron saw her and felt his heart leap, but he did not go forth to greet her. It was less fear of Seigneur Fitzalan's wrath that restrained him than the fear that her nearness would make him desire to be yet nearer and nearer, as the first cup of wine brings the desire for a second and a third.

Besides, even if Seigneur Fitzalan's anger could be avoided, the final parting was yet inevitable. And Alyx should surely take the more kindly to Talbot's bed if she were not still warmed by Kieron's touch.

So he watched her ride by and bit his lip and did nothing. And if, by chance, he should be abroad when she rode, he stood and lowered his head and bent a trifle from the waist, giving her courtesy as any man or prentice would.

For distraction, he busied himself with dangerous plans — the hot-air balloon. It was not to be a man-carrying balloon; for that would surely be defined as a machine by Holy Church. If, indeed, Holy Church should discover the matter. Which was not unlikely, for the Brothers of Ludd were feared as much as they were respected by the common folk; and many a man would inform against his neighbour if he thought that such action would improve his own prospects.

So a man-carrying balloon must not be attempted — yet. But a hot-air balloon that a prentice-boy could hold on the end of a cord — surely that could only be regarded as a toy? A clever toy, perhaps. But not a dangerous toy ... Kieron was so obsessed by his need to experiment with airborne devices that he stupidly chose to ignore the fact that Holy Church was already interested in his activities ...

At first, his design for the balloon was modest. It was to be no more than the height of a man, no wider than a wine cask; and it was to be constructed of four lengths of linen, cut to shape and sewn carefully over a light wooden frame. Where could all this be accomplished so that Master Hobart might remain in blessed ignorance and so that the curiosity of townsfolk would not be greatly tempted? Kieron consulted with Aylwin. Aylwin pondered the problem. It was similar to his own. He wished to be able to paint in freedom and seclusion without being scolded for wasting his time or jeered for attempting an art to which he was not contracted.

The solution was discovered by accident as Kieron and Aylwin walked together one day, discussing their projects, inland along the banks of the river Arun, far from the town that seemed, in the distance, to be squeezed between church and castle.

The solution to the problem was revealed in the form

76

of a derelict windmill, unused for a century or more, that stood near the river. According to legend, the miller and his entire family had been put to the stake for misusing the power of the wind. According to legend the derelict mill was haunted by their ghosts.

Aylwin knew something of the story, and repeated what he knew to Kieron. The miller had been an ambitious and ingenious man who believed that the winds of heaven were given to mankind to be used for whatever purposes mankind could devise. Holy Church permitted the use of the wind for the grinding of corn — necessary for human survival; for the pumping of fresh water — also necessary for human survival; and for the propulsion of ships — again necessary for human survival. The Church admitted the use of machines for necessities: it did not admit the use of machines for luxuries.

But the miller had used wind power not only to grind corn but to turn a lathe that his son might fashion goblets, bowls, platters from seasoned wood, these to be sold to the nobility, who admired purity of shape in all things, whether glass, stone, metal or wood. And he had further permitted wind power to be used to operate weaving machines so that his wife and daughter could produce linen and silk cloth, the like of which could not be found in many days' travel.

Envious people betrayed him to Holy Church. The four of them — man, wife, son and daughter — were burned on the same day at the same time, so positioned that, smoke permitting, they would witness each other's agony.

And so the mill had been left to rot, and left also to the occupancy of ghosts. It was known as Weaver's Mill. Few people cared to visit it in daylight or in darkness. Besides, when the Arun flooded, the lower part of the mill came under water.

Kieron looked at the derelict windmill, and thought of its ghosts, and loved them. Here was the place to construct his hot-air balloon. Here was the place where Aylwin could paint in peace.

"This is our home," he said. "Among the rats and the memories, this is our home. Here I will show you something of the art of oil colour. Here I will construct my hot-air balloon."

Aylwin was not happy. "Kieron, it is far from the town."

"That is good."

"Also, the spirits may not welcome us."

"You believe in spirits, Aylwin?"

Aylwin crossed himself. "I believe that there are things in which it is dangerous not to believe."

"Well, then, we are at one with the ghosts. They will be friendly to us, because we, too, rebel against our destinies."

"I am afraid," said Aylwin.

"So, also, am I. But is it not better to be filled with fear and do what one desires than to be filled with fear and achieve nothing?"

Aylwin had no answer. So Weaver's Mill became the refuge for a miller who wished to paint and for a painter who wished to fly.

14

IT TOOK KIERON many days to construct the hot-air balloon, which not only gave Alyx Fitzalan some moments of terror and brought Kieron himself to the brink of disaster but also changed the course of history.

Though Aylwin and Kieron were to share the derelict windmill for their separate purposes, Kieron was now resolved not to endanger his friend by involving him in this new project. Nor would he further endanger Sholto, though he would have been greatly glad of the smith's help in fashioning a small brazier. The message of Brother Sebastian had been clear. If anyone was to suffer because of Kieron's desire to reconquer the air, it must be himself alone.

He bought much coarse linen and quite astounded Master Hobart with his requirements of paper. The old man loved Kieron too well, and feared for his safety too much, to enquire closely into the reasons for his demands. Master Hobart chose to remind himself that Kieron was one of the great ones, that *Mistress Fitzalan's Leap* was a masterpiece by any standard, and that great ones were privileged to indulge their madnesses as best they may. Hobart drank more, coughed more and prayed more. But, otherwise, he did and said nothing.

So Kieron transported his linen and paper and needles and thread to the derelict mill; and he bought an old fire-basket from a tinker who was amazed to receive five silver pennies for a piece of useless iron. And Kieron went to work like a man possessed. He bound willow wands to make a frame — slender shoots whose suppleness was ideal

79

for his purpose. Weight, Kieron had discerned, was all. The frame of the balloon must be so light that the hot air would triumph.

Meanwhile, Alyx rode daily, hoping to encounter Kieron at least once more before she was taken to Chichester to lie with a sad young man who was not long for this world. And meanwhile, Aylwin, whenever he was released from his duties, came to the mill to paint.

Kieron gave him instruction. Aylwin was a ready pupil: Kieron was a good teacher. Aylwin learned to paint land and sky with fire in his brush. His canvases became alive with colour and movement. Truly, Kieron saw, there was a great talent in the prentice miller. It was a pity that he was doomed to spend his life grinding corn.

Meanwhile, the construction of the hot-air balloon progressed. And Kieron's ambitions waxed bolder. The balloon would be twice the height of a man and twice the width of a wine cask. It would be a great balloon — no longer a toy but a declaration of intent.

Meanwhile, Mistress Alyx continued to ride. And one day she rode out along the bank of the river Arun, as far as Weaver's Mill, seeking the boy whose face haunted her dreams. And that was the day that the balloon was ready for its flight.

The balloon, slack and flapping, hung suspended from a wooden beam jutting out of a window in the mill until the heat rising from the glowing charcoal in the brazier should cause the air inside it to expand and become buoyant. When the balloon was extended and ready to rise, Kieron would release its fastenings and control its ascent by a long stout cord fastened to a length of metal wire, fastened in turn to the brazier suspended under the balloon.

Aylwin was busy sketching Kieron at work, as he checked the fastenings and blew the charcoal with bellows to a white heat. Neither of them noticed Alyx, as she rode along the bank of the Arun, until she had almost reached the mill.

"Ludd ha' mercy," exclaimed Aylwin in fright. "The seigneur's daughter is upon us." He tried to conceal his drawing materials as if he had been detected in the commission of a serious crime.

"Rest easy, my friend," said Kieron, glancing up. "Mistress Alyx will cause us no difficulties, I promise." He had not told Aylwin — indeed, he had not told anyone — of the intimacies that had passed between him and Alyx. These were matters best remembered — or forgot — only by those who had experienced them.

Alyx dismounted. "Well, Kieron, I wondered where you hid yourself. What is this contraption that commands all your attention?"

"A hot-air balloon, Mistress Alyx." His tone was deferential, as it always had been when others were present. "A toy, a whim, nothing more."

"So," said Alyx, "we have here a prentice painter who does not paint and a prentice miller who does not grind corn. Most curious." She turned to Aylwin. "Boy, walk my horse somewhat, then let him graze. I have ridden him passing hard."

"Yes, Mistress." Aylwin took the bridle and led the hunter away.

Alyx waited until he was out of earshot. "Kieron, I have sought you for many days. Why do you humiliate me?"

"Beloved Alyx, I do not humiliate you."

"You do not come to the castle."

"I have no reason. Also, your father has commanded me."

"He knows about us?"

"I do not know how, but he knows about us." Kieron smiled. "He told me that you wept somewhat . . ."

"It is a lie," said Alyx fiercely. "I would not weep for a prentice painter."

"Of this I am convinced," said Kieron tranquilly. "Yet your father is an honest man. He must be mistaken."

She flung her arms round him, not caring if Aylwin saw or saw not. "Kieron, I love you."

"Darling Alyx, I love you also. But our paths diverge. You wed with Talbot, I wed with Petrina. You are high born, I am low born. There is nothing we can do."

"We will see about that," said Alyx. "Talbot will be dead within a year, that I promise."

"You would kill him?"

"He will die, Kieron. That is all. He will die . . . What of Petrina?"

Kieron kissed her and held her close. "Alyx, we deal in idle dreams. You must know that."

Alyx dabbed at her eyes. "Yes, we must be what we are." She stood back. "The miller's boy — will he be a teller of tales?"

"Rest easy. He is my friend. I teach him a new art."

Alyx tried to laugh. "He is not the only one you have taught a new art, Kieron-head-in-the-air . . . See, your balloon fills out like a fat marrow. It strains to rise."

"Ludd's Grief! Excuse me, Alyx. I must cast loose up above." He dashed into the mill, loosened the top of the balloon; and took the wood beam in from the window. Then he came down and regarded the balloon critically.

It was in truth like a huge marrow, bigger than he had imagined. The charcoal in the brazier suspended beneath it glowed brightly. The balloon swayed in a light breeze, straining at its mooring.

Alyx marvelled at the sight. "How will you explain this toy to Holy Church, Kieron?"

"How should I need explain it?" he demanded bitterly. "It is but a toy, and I am but a fool called Kieron-head-in-the-air."

"The neddies might call it a machine. They might think you guilty of machinism."

"Hang the stupid neddies!" Kieron carefully loosened the mooring, and the balloon rose. He paid out the cord that held it very cautiously, delighting in the strong pull on his arms. The balloon rose above the windmill. Aylwin had tethered Alyx's horse to a stunted thorn bush and stood hands on hips, mouth open, observing the wondrous sight.

Kieron felt the delicious pull of the cord — the pull that strove to free him from the confines of earth — and rejoiced in it. Impulsively, he jumped. The balloon instantly responded, lifting him over Alyx's head, gently returning him to the ground.

"Bravo! Bravo!" cried Alyx. "What a toy we have here. Let me try, Kieron. Please let me try."

"You will have to hold firmly," he cautioned. "The pull is stronger than you think . . . No, Alyx, perhaps it is best that you do not meddle with this thing."

"Don't spoil the sport, Kieron. I must hold it. I shall. I am not a child."

"Nor is it a toy for a child," he warned. "Well, hold the cord, so. And wrap it round your wrist, so."

Carefully, he gave the cord to her, and made sure that she held it firmly. As she felt the pull, Alyx gave a cry of delight. Then she prepared to jump as Kieron had done. Unfortunately, as she jumped, there was a sudden gust of wind. The balloon responded to it. Also, Kieron had forgotten that Alyx was much lighter than he.

Hanging on to the cord for dear life, she rose majestically into the air — but did not come down. The balloon drifted smoothly over the grassland, rising a little.

Alyx screamed.

Kieron was horrified.

"Jump!" he called. "Let go the cord! Let go!"

She either did not hear him or she was past hearing. She hung on desperately with both hands, kicking her legs frantically as if the very action would compel her return to earth.

Aylwin gazed at the scene petrified. Then he sank to his knees and began to pray.

Fortunately, the ascent of the balloon was very slow. It had risen no more than about three or four metres from the ground when Alyx either had the wit to let go or

83

could hold on to the cord no longer. Kieron had been running after her, shouting his exhortations. Indeed, he leaped high, trying to grab her feet. When she fell, she landed almost in his arms, knocking him to the ground. Kieron was winded, but Alyx had hurt her ankle. She sat on the damp earth, whimpering a little, exploring the damage to her leg, and looked to Kieron for comfort.

He stroked her hair and mumbled words of comfort. But his eyes were on the balloon. Freed of its unwilling human ballast, the hot-air balloon rose majestically, trailing its cord like a long limp tail. The wind caused the charcoal in the brazier to burn more fiercely; and this, in turn, gave the balloon greater lift. It rose rapidly to about two hundred metres, then began to drift towards Arundel.

Kieron watched fascinated, full of pride. Truly, he had created a formidable thing. Had the balloon been only half as big again, he could have harnessed it to a basket in which he himself sat; and then he might have ridden through the sky like a god — or, at least, like one of the First Men.

"Kieron, my leg hurts."

"Yes, love. I will attend to it." But his eyes remained on the balloon.

"I'm wet, and there is mud on my clothes."

"Yes, Alyx. Soon you will be warm and dry," he soothed, "and I will take you to the castle." But his eyes remained on the balloon.

"I hate you!" she stormed.

"Yes, love. Most reasonable. I am a hateful person." Still he watched the balloon.

"I love you! You are a fool but — Ludd help me — I love you." She kissed him and held him close.

"Darling Alyx, indeed I am a fool. But I have achieved something this day."

The balloon, having drifted over Arundel, now seemed to exhibit a will of its own. It changed direction and hovered over the castle. Then, apparently convinced that it had achieved its proper destination, it burst spectacularly into flame and fell in burning remnants upon the ancestral home of Seigneur Fitzalan.

Aylwin had recovered himself sufficiently to come running after Kieron. But when he saw what had happened to the balloon, he sank to his knees once more. "Ludd ha' mercy! Ludd ha' mercy! Kieron, oh Kieron, you have done for us."

Kieron smiled at him benignly. "Aylwin, my friend, first collect your wits. Then collect your painting materials from the mill and return with some discretion to your master. You have not been here this day. You have not seen me or Mistress Alyx. You understand?"

"I understand, Kieron. But we are sworn in friendship."

"Then let us maintain the bond. You shall not be put at risk for an accident such as this." He turned to Alyx. "Mistress Alyx, have you seen Aylwin, the miller's prentice, this day?" He was holding her in his arms, and he knew that Aylwin would see how he was holding her.

Alyx's cheeks became red. "Not if you require it, Kieron," she said softly. "I have not seen the miller's prentice this day."

"Well, Aylwin," pursued Kieron, "by the same token, you have not seen Mistress Alyx and myself. For if you claim that you have, I will surely kill you."

Aylwin was offended. "We are sworn. Was that necessary?"

"Forgive me, Aylwin. I do not think clearly. Events move too fast. Now go."

Alyx tried to stand up, cried out with pain and fell down again. "The ankle — it swells mightily, and the pain is worse ... What shall we do, Kieron? What shall we do?"

"If I were to put you on your horse, could you ride back?"

"Perhaps. I think so."

He bent down and lifted her gently, then he carried her to where the horse was tethered. It was a greater distance than he had thought, and Alyx — though light — was still somewhat heavier than he had thought. The exertion strained his limbs and his lungs. He set Alyx down on the grass and waited to recover himself before lifting her on to the horse.

Alyx surveyed her swollen ankle, and her dirty clothes with a look of despair. "How shall I explain all this?" she cried. "What a state I am in!"

"You fell," suggested Kieron. "You fell from the horse."

"I never fall," she retorted regally. "Is it not known that I am the best horsewoman in the south country?"

"Nevertheless, Alyx, today you fell. The truth will assist neither of us. Neither your father nor Talbot must ever learn that you rose perilously over the meadow on the end of a hot-air balloon."

"What if I were seen?"

Kieron shrugged. "The word of a commoner against the word of a Fitzalan? Besides, you could not have been seen, except with a spy-glass."

"My father's watchman has a spy-glass. He reports on the arrival of vessels for trade."

"Then he will not report on the antics of an unwilling aeronaut," said Kieron patiently. "Also, you were aloft so little time, and it would not be possible to discern your identity from such a distance." He grinned. "Particularly since you thrashed about so — behaviour which Mistress Alyx Fitzalan would never stoop, or rise, to... We must take some chance, Alyx. If, indeed, a figure were seen, I will plead guilty. It was, after all, my balloon... Come, I will lift you to the saddle." He managed to get her seated in reasonable comfort on the horse without too much exertion.

She looked down at him unhappily. "What will they do to you, my love?"

"I not know," he answered, affecting small concern. "Likely there will be some tedious penance. But, swear that whatever happens, you will admit no knowledge of this matter."

"Kieron, how can I so swear when I know not what they will do to you."

"Because I require it, for your sake, for mine, and for that of poor Aylwin who is now half out of his mind with fright."

She sighed. "Then I so swear; but I am afraid."

"Smile, Alyx. That is how I would always remember you."

"Shall we meet again before — before I wed?"

"Ludd knows. I do not... Alyx, it is within the month is it not?"

"Seventeen days hence... I love you."

"I love you also. Go now, and let us each remember the other's love with gladness."

Sadly, Alyx turned her horse towards Arundel. Kieron watched her for a while, then returned to the mill. There were materials and tools to be put away and the place made tidy. And there was much thinking to be done. Was it better to go to the castle and confess to the balloon, or was it better to let Seigneur Fitzalan's men seek him out? It would not take them long. Such an adventure, everyone knew, could only be the work of Kieron-head-in-the-air. Therefore, better to make a virtue out of necessity and explain matters to Seigneur Fitzalan before the neddies intervened.

But Kieron was out of luck. The castle watchman was not the only man to use a spy-glass. Brother Sebastian possessed one, and frequently employed it from the cathedral tower to inform himself of the affairs of the world.

15

KIERON DID NOT know how long he had been chained to the wall. He did not know whether it was night or day. He knew only that he was in a cell in the Luddite House of Correction and that his case might even merit the attention of the Inquisitor General. It was a long time, he had been told, since anyone had been charged with attempting to construct a flying machine. The matter, therefore, was of more than local interest.

On the day his hot-air balloon had lifted Mistress Alyx across the meadow and had then risen grandly only to descend in fiery fragments on the castle, Kieron had not managed to get as far as making his apologies and explanations to Seigneur Fitzalan. The neddies were waiting for him: Brother Sebastian and Brother Hildebrand and Brother Lemuel.

They charged him with heresy and arrested him in the name of the Divine Boy. He was marched ignominiously through Arundel at sword-point. And that was the last he saw of daylight.

Brothers Hildebrand and Lemuel would have been satisfied to frighten Kieron a little, considering his construction of the hot-air balloon to be hardly more than an ambitious prank. After all, the boy was almost a full year from his majority; and his transgression need not be regarded as a deliberate assault upon doctrine.

But Brother Sebastian was ambitious. It was his intention to rise high in the Luddite Church. And a man could not rise high unless he distinguished himself early. The way to advancement was by high connection — which

Brother Sebastian did not possess — or by the revealing of significant heresy. Brother Sebastian prayed devoutly that Kieron would be revealed as a significant heretic.

True, Kieron was not yet a man. But heresy was no affliction of age. Brother Sebastian was aware that it was less than thirty years since a boy of thirteen had been burnt at the stake for harnessing the steam from a boiling kettle. The offence had been described by the Inquisitor General of the time as the attempted construction of a turbine, whatever that was.

Kieron's offence was more easy to define. He had attempted to construct a machine that would lift a man — or a woman — from the face of the earth. If that was not an heretical act, then Brother Sebastian would eat his habit. Already he was beginning to feel secure in his attitude. The spy-glass had revealed that it was not Kieron dangling from the infernal machine, but a woman.

Shortly after this observation, Brother Sebastian had noticed Mistress Alyx returning to the castle on horseback, but in a somewhat distressed condition.

She asserted that she had been thrown. But everyone knew that it was most unlikely for Mistress Alyx to be thrown. Brother Sebastian pondered the problem. Recently, Kieron had spent much time at the castle, executing studies for Master Hobart's brilliant painting of *Mistress Fitzalan's Leap*. Kieron and Mistress Alyx were almost of an age. Where there is smoke, it is hardly reckless to assume the presence of a fire.

Brother Sebastian had the wit to realise that Alyx Fitzalan was beyond his reach. Holy Church was not yet ready to directly challenge the feudal power of the seigneurs. But Kieron alone should be sufficient for Brother Sebastian's purpose. Having access to the castle and to the presence of Seigneur Fitzalan and Mistress Alyx, the boy could hardly be considered to be on the same level of insignificance as a common field labourer. Also, much could be made of his association with Mistress Alyx. Much could be made of it without much actually being said. Besides, if necessary, some importance could be attached to the matter of the book. At the very least, it was an effective means of silencing any protest from the Fitzalans.

After arresting Kieron, Brother Sebastian had speedily armed himself with a warrant for searching; and he had gone to Master Hobart's house, there to terrorise the old man somewhat in the hope that he might betray himself as a partner to the heresy, and also to search Kieron's chamber.

He succeeded in terrifying Master Hobart only into hysteria and a great fit of coughing. He did, however, find the book, hidden under Kieron's mattress. That the book concerned the history of forbidden machines was significant, that it was hidden, though badly, was of even greater significance, and that its leather cover bore the imprint of the Fitzalan device was of the greatest significance of all.

Let the Seigneur beware, thought Brother Sebastian comfortably. If he attempted to interfere with divine justice in any way, he might find that he was in danger of scorching his noble fingers.

Brother Sebastian was tasting the heady delights of power. He had written an account of the affair to the office of the Inquisitor General in London and confidently expected that he would receive authorisation to proceed with a full trial for heresy.

Meanwhile, he had Kieron chained to the wall in the House of Correction. He did not relish the boy's discomfort. To do so would have been an unpardonable sin. Brother Sebastian convinced himself that he was concerned only with the salvation of Kieron's spirit. If Kieron should burn for his transgression — which Ludd forbid, if at all possible — it were better that he burned in enlightenment, in a proper state of mind, knowing that his sin would be forgiven if he showed true penitence.

So Brother Sebastian held much converse with his

prisoner, seeking to distinguish diabolical intent from youthful indiscretion. Kieron was not entirely helpful. At least, he was not helpful to himself, though perhaps he furthered Brother Sebastian's unacknowledged aims.

"Do you resent me, Kieron?" Brother Sebastian asked the question while sitting on a stool, sipping from a glass of tea.

Kieron, who had survived on bread, offal and cold water for several days, still had his wits about him.

"Why should I resent you, Brother Sebastian? You do your duty, and in that you have my respect, even my admiration."

"So. We understand each other. I do not wish to punish you. I wish to save you."

"This, I perceive. You act from the best intentions." Kieron smiled. "I would much prefer to be saved rather than punished."

"The hot-air balloon is a grievous sin. It is a machine, Kieron. A machine not authorised by Holy Church. You must see that it is the duty of the Church to protect the people from the wickedness and the temptation of machines. You know your history, boy. Machines have corrupted the world twice. They shall not do so a third time." Brother Sebastian sipped his tea noisily.

Kieron licked his lips. He could not remember when he had last tasted anything warm. "I was aware of no wickedness, Brother. The hot-air balloon was but a foolish toy which served to pass the time."

"So?" Brother Sebastian looked at him coldly. "There is also the matter of the book. Who gave it to you, Kieron? The book about flying machines."

This was the first time Brother Sebastian had mentioned the book. Kieron, tired, cold, depressed, was taken by surprise. His mouth fell open. He thought of Alyx. Even she might not be safe from this black crow.

"You do not answer, Kieron. Do you wish to shield someone?"

"I wish to shield no one but myself. I borrowed the book. I — I intended to return it."

"Seigneur Fitzalan gave you leave to take the book from his library?"

"No."

"Someone else, then?"

"No."

"Yet you say you borrowed the book."

"Yes."

"Without the owner's permission?"

"I intended to return it."

"For that, I have only your word in these present sad circumstances. It is also possible to interpret such borrowing as stealing. A reasonable man might conclude that you had stolen the book with the intention of constructing one or more of the machines described therein."

"Ludd damn you!" exploded Kieron. "Destroy learning, if you must. Destroy progress, if you must. Burn me, if you must. But do not sicken me with words."

Brother Sebastian emptied his glass of tea and looked sad. "The damnation of Ludd is reserved only for those who construct machines with evil intent. Burn you may, Kieron. I will not deny the possibility. It would sadden me, but Ludd's will be done. However, I am your friend, your brother, and I shall save your soul. And in that, there will be some consolation."

Whereupon, Brother Sebastian left Kieron to his thoughts.

16

THE INQUISITOR GENERAL found that there was a charge
to answer and authorised a trial for heresy. The trial
would begin, as was customary, on the first day of the
next lunar month. If a verdict of guilty were given, the
sentence would be carried out on the last day of the same
lunar month.

Meanwhile, the conditions under which Kieron was held
improved. He was no longer chained to the wall of his
cell. He was given a bed of straw, a table and a chair.
He was allowed one hot meal a day, and he was further
allowed to have visitors and to call upon witnesses who
might testify to his character. Holy Church allowed these
things so that none might complain of partiality or im-
pediment. It was true that few were ever acquitted of
the charge of heresy. Holy Church rarely held such a
public trial unless the facts were incontrovertible. Nevertheless, justice must be seen to be done.

Kieron's first visitors were his parents. Kristen came
red-eyed with weeping. Gerard came full of hope, smell-
ing of resin and wood shavings, convinced that too much
had been made of a boyish prank.

"Kieron, child, how do they feed you?" sniffed Kristen.
"Do they feed you well?"

Kieron noticed that her hair was fully white, though
she could be barely thirty-five years old. Yet there was
beauty in her face and dignity in her carriage. He was
immensely sorry for the pain he had caused.

"Yes, mother," he lied. "I eat excellently and want
for nothing."

"You are an artist," exploded Gerard, "a great artist. Master Hobart himself has said so." He gazed at the straw bed and the bare walls of the cell. "How dare they keep a man with a golden future in this place? Are you guilty of the charge, boy? Speak plainly. We who begot you have a right to know."

"Sir," said Kieron carefully, knowing that Brother Sebastian had his ear to the cell door, "I constructed a toy for my amusement. A hot-air balloon. I did not know that Holy Church could be offended by so trivial a matter."

Gerard stroked his chin thoughtfully. "It was rash, boy. But it can hardly be sinful. The Church likes nothing new — quite rightly. The fault lies surely in those who have instructed you... I have heard that *Mistress Fitzalan's Leap* is a masterpiece, though I know nought of such things. Master Hobart has said that it could not have been accomplished without you."

"Master Hobart is generous," said Kieron, "but there may be a grain of truth in his words."

Gerard held him close. "Do not fear, boy. The charge will be dismissed, and those who brought it will suffer the consequences."

"I bear no animosity to anyone," said Kieron, chiefly for Brother Sebastian. "My hope is that Holy Church will establish my innocence and permit me to continue my appointed work."

Gerard clapped his shoulder. "Well spoken! I knew! I knew! You are but a high-spirited lad, and it is all a great misunderstanding."

But Kristen was wiser. She held Kieron close to her and stroked his hair. "Are you afraid, little one?" she whispered.

"Yes, mother, I am afraid."

"You know what they will do?"

"Yes, mother. I know what they will do."

"Be at peace, Kieron. We will die together. And if there is another life, we will share it also."

94

"Hold, woman!" stormed Gerard. "Kieron will live."

Kristen stood back, having achieved a strange serenity. "Yes, Gerard, Kieron will live. Of that I am sure."

"By the Hammer of Ludd, and by my hammer also he will indeed live," swore Gerard. "He will live to bury those who would besmirch his name."

The gaoler rapped on the door.

"We will come again," said Kristen. "We will come tomorrow. I will bring scones and fresh butter and the blackberry preserve you like."

When they had gone, Brother Sebastian entered the cell. "Your father has a strong voice," he said carefully.

Kieron smiled faintly. "A strong mind and a strong right arm also. He is a good and simple man."

"Yet he utters dangerous words."

"My father is an honest man, as all in the seigneurie know," retorted Kieron calmly. "He deceives no one, commits no sins. His honesty is his armour."

"What do you mean by that, boy?"

"Only, Brother Sebastian, that you have one bird in your trap. You will not snare another from the same nest."

Petrina came to visit him also, accompanied by her father, which was proper.

Sholto, a huge man of few words and great good will, was tongue-tied. Petrina, buxom and ripe for the marriage that would only have been months away, did most of the talking.

"Kieron, you look dreadful pale. Do you have enough to eat?"

He smiled. "Truly, women are alike. My mother's first thought was for my stomach."

"There are certain differences," flashed Petrina, "which presently you will perceive."

"I am sorry. I did not mean to rebuke you." Kieron turned to the smith. "Sholto, it was kind of you to come, and to bring Petrina. I am grateful. Neither I nor my

95

father will be offended if you now wish to dissolve the contract."

Sholto shuffled his feet awkwardly, and looked at the floor, at the walls, at the ceiling, as if seeking divine guidance. None came.

"Kieron, boy, I like you well. This is a sorry matter which, in truth, I do not understand. I understand how to work iron and steel, but not much else. Solvig, my wife, deals with other affairs." He cast an anxious glance at his daughter. "And now, alas, so does Petrina. At the forge, I am master." He shrugged. "But with women, who can argue?"

"Dissolve the contract!" exploded Petrina, tossing back her hair, thrusting out her firm breasts. "Do you wish to dissolve the contract, Kieron-head-in-the-air?"

Kieron was baffled. The child he had known was now demonstrably a woman. He had assumed she would wish to be quit of a heretic, who would likely burn. But one should never assume with a woman.

"I did but think to save you some unpleasantness."

"You think but little," snapped Petrina. "Otherwise, you would not have thought to construct stupid kites and hot-air balloons. And you would not have thought to embroil yourself with the Fitzalans."

"Petrina, speak carefully," said Kieron, mindful of Brother Sebastian's ear at the door. "These walls are thin. Voices carry."

"Poof!" said Petrina. "So voices carry. Everyone knows that Alyx Fitzalan is besotted with you." She gave a faint smile. "Even Brother Sebastian has ears."

"Brother Sebastian has excellent hearing," confirmed Kieron. "Even in this cell, I suspect, our conversation does not pass unheard."

"No matter," said Petrina calmly. "There is nothing to be hid. Do you wish to be released from the contract?"

"No, by Ned Ludd. I would wed with you, Petrina. In happier circumstances, I would wed with you joyously."

Petrina smiled. "Then there is no problem, Kieron. I would wed with you. So be it."

"You are still convinced that the astrologer Marcus foretold truly?"

"Yes, I am convinced. Besides, Kieron, whatever else Holy Church may do, it acknowledges the validity of contracts. This I have discovered, at some effort."

"So?"

"So, Kieron, if we are both willing, the Inquisitor General may be petitioned to suspend punishment until I am with child — or until it is seen that I cannot conceive."

Kieron was dumbfounded. "You would do this for me?"

"You are my contracted husband. Could I do less?"

Kieron laughed. "The astrologer Marcus may yet win the day."

"Do not mock men of science."

"But how do you know this — about punishment being suspended?"

"It does not matter how I know. Also the thing is not certain. Much depends upon the pleasure of the Inquisitor General. I know only that it has happened before." She smiled grimly. "Holy Church even has power to advance the contracted day of marriage so that the day of punishment shall not be over-delayed."

"How, then?" Kieron was perplexed. "I would be allowed my freedom until I had got you with child?"

"No, stupid. I would be allowed to share your cell. There are limits to benevolence."

"You would wed with a heretic and live in a prison? You would be branded for ever."

"I would also be widowed for ever. But that is my choice, Kieron. Do you complain of it?"

"No, I — that is, Petrina, my dear, it is too much to ask of you."

"So. No one has asked it. Let your conscience rest easy."

Sholto rubbed his hands nervously. "Argue not with a female, Kieron. You will have the worst of it."

"Do you still wish your daughter to wed with me?"

Sholto scratched his head. "A contract is a contract, for good or ill." He glanced at his daughter. "What a woman wants, that she will get, as I know to my cost."

Petrina said: "Let us not waste time. It is settled. That is all there is to it ... Kieron, many will speak for you; and it will carry weight that I am still willing to wed with you." She moved close to him and whispered: "Can you feign madness?"

He looked at her, aghast. "Can I — " She placed a hand over his mouth. "I am told," she whispered, "that a plea of temporary madness might be acceptable to Holy Church — particularly if there were those who testified to such fits."

"You are well informed," said Kieron softly. "You are well informed about many things. Who has spoken to you, Petrina?"

She put her mouth to his ear. "A lady came riding. Need I say more?"

Alyx! Alyx Fitzalan cared about him enough to persuade Petrina. His head was in a whirl.

The gaoler knocked on the door.

"We will come again, Kieron," said Petrina. "I am sure my father will wish to escort me here tomorrow. I will bring a bacon and egg pie, hot from the oven, and I will watch you eat it."

"Petrina, I would kiss you." Kieron glanced hesitantly at Sholto.

The smith laughed. "Kiss her, then, boy. Kiss her well. It is the only way you will ever beat a woman."

Somewhat later on the same day, Hobart came, a shawl round his shoulders, racked by coughing, clutching a flask of spirit.

"Kieron, my dear son, how do they treat you?"

"Well enough, Master Hobart. I am alive and healthy, as you see."

"You are thinner. You are pale."

"I do not crave for weight. My only lack is sunlight."

"You shall have it, my dear son, you shall have it. I have signed a statement and had it witnessed that it was upon my insistence that you constructed the hot-air balloon. I required its construction for a painting, and that is the truth. I required to have a sketch of the castle from the air."

Kieron was near to weeping. "Father, you cannot do this thing. You shall not put yourself at risk in such a manner."

With some effort, Hobart drew himself up straight. "And who shall prevent me, boy? You have called me Father, of which I am proud. And is it not the duty of a father to protect his son, even if that son be not of the flesh but of the spirit?"

"A son — a spiritual son — also has a duty," Kieron pointed out. "I beg you to destroy the document. It is dangerous."

"Dangerous! Poof!" Master Hobart took a sip of spirit. "Forgive me, Kieron. This physic is necessary for an old man who has outlived his strengths and skills... All my life, Kieron, I have lived safely — and in fear. In fear of those who employ me, in fear of the loss of my poor talent. There comes a time when a man desires to rise above fear. Such a time is when he wishes to protect one he loves... Forgive me. I am not courageous. Forgive me for deriving courage from a flask... But, I have been in the presence of greatness. I am content. Do you understand? I have seen you make brush strokes that have a wild and savage beauty. I know that you will travel far... I wish you to paint, for in that you have a great gift. But if it is your pleasure to reach for the stars, I will accept it. I cannot understand it. I cannot say more. But I accept it. Do we understand each other?"

"We understand each other, my father."

"Well, then, there is no more to be said." Hobart took a deep draught of the spirit. "I have outlived my strength and my skills, but I have not entirely outlived my usefulness. The document will stand, Kieron, though I fall." Hobart smiled. "Once I tried to buy you from your parents. You did not know that. Now, I do not wish to buy you. I am content only to pay a very small price for your freedom."

Kieron could no longer hold back the tears. "Sir, you destroy me with love."

Hobart smiled. "I have watched you grow with love. I have tutored you with love. I will not destroy you with love . . . Kieron, I doubt that I shall visit you again. My health, you understand?"

"I understand."

"Therefore, kiss me, my son. It is but little to you. It means much to me, because I am a foolish old man."

Kieron drew close and kissed him on the forehead.

"On the lips, my son."

"So be it. On the lips."

"Now we are truly united in resolve." Hobart seemed happy. "Farewell, Kieron. You will not burn. Rest easy."

"Then I shall live to complete my apprenticeship," said Kieron lightly.

Hobart gave a faint smile. "Your apprenticeship ended with *Mistress Fitzalan's Leap*. It is a great painting. I can teach you no more."

Master Hobart took some more spirit. Then he left the cell. Two days later he was discovered dead, hanging by the neck from a beam in his chamber.

17

IN TIMES TO come, Kieron recalled the last few days he spent in the House of Correction almost with pleasure. They were the last days of the world he had known, the last days of order and security, the last days of peace.

Gerard and Kristen came to visit him again. So did Petrina and, with some apprehension, Aylwin the miller's apprentice.

Aylwin knew nothing of the measures being taken to defend Kieron. He looked upon his friend with much pity, as if the smell of smoke were already in his nostrils.

"So, Kieron, it is in a sorry condition that I find you."

Kieron laughed. "Not so sorry as all that. I have food, I sleep well, my friends and loved ones do not neglect me."

Alywin nodded towards the cell door, fully aware that there was a patient listener. "I have not broken my bond word, Kieron."

"Good, my friend. Neither have I. Nor will I. Let us each rest easy."

Aylwin seemed relieved. He had no wish to be noticed in any way by Holy Church. "Many will be willing to speak for you. I among them, if you require it."

Kieron noted the unhappiness in Aylwin's eyes, and knew that it had cost him much to make the offer. "Aylwin, I thank you. I do not despise your kindness, yet I think that stronger voices may be heard in my favour."

"If the worst comes to the worst —" began Alywin.

"It will not." Kieron also nodded towards the cell door.

Then he said prophetically: "I will live to bury some who bear me small good will. This I swear."

Aylwin shuffled his feet. "I must go now."

"Do not neglect the skills you have learned. You have some talent, as I know."

Aylwin shrugged. Where now would he obtain the materials and instruction he needed? "We are each called to our destiny, friend. I will come again." He held out his hand. "Also, I will think much upon you, Kieron. You are my true friend."

But Aylwin did not come to the House of Correction again; and when Kieron next saw him, he was less a hand — the painting hand. And his black hair was streaked with white.

Alyx Fitzalan was the last visitor Kieron received. She was accompanied by her father's bailiff, who by his demeanour made plain his hearty disapproval of the encounter.

"Be upstanding in the presence of Mistress Alyx Fitzalan," he intoned. An unnecessary command, since Kieron was already standing.

"Kentigern," said Mistress Alyx with some tartness in her voice, "go and keep company with the good Brother Sebastian, whose heavy breathing informs me of his nearness. Discuss with him whatever is dear to you, and benefit from his pure and learned mind."

"But, Mistress, Seigneur Fitzalan commanded me to remain within your hearing."

"Do that, then. My hearing is excellent. I can hear the good Brother Sebastian shaking like one afflicted. Perhaps he has received a vision. Enquire of him if this be the case."

Kentigern retired, discomfitted. For a moment or two, Kieron heard him exchanging words with Brother Sebastian on the other side of the cell door.

"Well, Kieron?"

"Well, Mistress Alyx?"

They gazed at each other, each resisting the impulse

to come close and hold close. It would not do. The witnesses at the keyhole would report what they saw.

"So you stole a book from my father's library. At least, that is what I am told." But her eyes said: Thank you, my love, for protecting me.

Kieron signified his understanding. "I am bitterly sorry, Mistress Alyx. I intended to borrow it for a short time only."

"Did you know that it contained heresy?"

"No, Mistress. Being simple, I thought only to take a book to read. I intended to restore it at the first opportunity."

"My father thinks you are a fool, Kieron. A fool without malice."

"So I am, Mistress. Definitely a fool. But I have no malice."

"So I will testify," said Alyx. "You have a great talent for falling off gentle horses, Kieron. The talent of a fool. Nevertheless, I am capricious enough to defer my wedding so that I may speak for you. Perhaps I am foolish also."

Kieron knelt and kissed her hand. He would have kissed her lips and felt her breasts against him. But he was mindful of the watchers and the listeners.

"Mistress, you are indeed foolish to concern yourself with my predicament. Though I am nothing to you, I am most grateful for your interest in my case."

Alyx smiled sadly. "Stand, Kieron. The artist knows his subject. The subject knows the artist. Between them, formality is tedious."

"Mistress, I — " Kieron glanced at the cell door.

"Yes, I know. The ears flap. Master Kentigern grows red in the face, and the good Brother Sebastian breathes hard. It is of little importance ... My father bids me thank you for removing the book from his library."

"How so?"

"It is simple. He did not know that he possessed an heretical work. He is glad to be quit of it. Also, he, too, will speak for you. He bade me say that, while he supports Holy Church in the rooting out of heresy, fools are with us always and may be relied upon to accomplish their own destruction."

"He is most kind." Kieron, remembering his last encounter with Fitzalan, thought the seigneur was exceptionally kind.

"He is, above all, a practical man," said Alyx enigmatically. "He is prepared to pay a reasonable price to achieve his ends ... Kieron, I have news for you. It is both bad and good."

Kieron knew before she told it. "Master Hobart?"

"Is dead. He left a document."

"I know. How did he die?"

"He hanged himself ... Holy Church will not burn you. The document absolves you from blame. Add to this those who will speak for you, and the Church is powerless."

Kieron was weeping. He turned towards the cell door. "Brother Sebastian," he shouted, "you hear me! Better for you to leave the seigneurie if I am acquitted. For if you do not — "

"Kieron!" Alyx spoke sharply. "Indulge your grief, but do not undo the work for which a good man died."

Kieron hid his face in his hands. "Alyx, I am sorry. Hobart was as a father to me, and — "

"And," said Alyx, "he will be remembered for his last work, which was his greatest. You gave him some assistance, I recall. You are his monument, Kieron. Be worthy of him. That is all."

Kieron looked at her, red-eyed, the tears streaming down his face. "I will try to be worthy of him. But who can say if I succeed?"

"Time will reveal, Kieron. I must go now." She smiled, and suddenly threw caution to the winds "My father drives a close bargain ... But kiss me, so that I will remember it."

Kieron was aghast. "But, Brother Sebastian?"

"Brother Sebastian is of little account, now. His days are numbered. And Kentigern is true to the house of Fitzalan. Kiss me. Indulge a woman's fancy. I have dreams, premonitions." She shuddered. "Kiss me."

Kieron held her close, felt the warm young breasts against him, kissed her lips, her cheek, her ear, her neck. He, also, had premonitions. He knew that he would not hold the living Alyx Fitzalan again.

18

KIERON SLEPT BADLY, tormented by dreams. He was a child, with Petrina, in late summer. There was some question of following bees to find their honey, or to seek apples and plums. Eventually, they decided on apples and plums.

The dream dissolved. Now it was a fine October morning, with the sky blue, and the castle rising out of the mist; and the boy Kieron, carrying a deerhide bag, was walking to Master Hobart's house. He saw a dandelion clock, plucked the stem and blew the seeds away through the still air.

A great voice that seemed to fill the world said: "So you want to fly, do you?"

Kieron, terrified, looked all around him. There was no one to be seen. But it seemed advisable to make an answer. "Yes, I want to fly."

There was laughter. "Birds fly. Men walk. Put away such dreams."

Again he could see no one. Frightened, he continued on his way to the house of the painter.

Mist and darkness. Then more sunlight. He was riding through the sky, then falling, falling. The sea was cold and there was a sharp pain in his leg.

And suddenly, Brother Sebastian was looking at him. Brother Sebastian's face was as large as the castle. His eyes were cold. "Heresy, Kieron! Men burn for heresy. Burn! Burn! Burn!"

Brother Sebastian's face became a black fog. No, not a fog. A column of smoke. Kieron could smell the smoke.

It was choking him. He cried out, opened his eyes. But he could still smell the smoke, and the cell was entirely dark. Now he was aware of noises, shouts, screams, the sound of thunder. Or was it something other than thunder?

His mind would not work, but the smoke was real. In the darkness, he coughed agonisingly and his eyes streamed tears. He needed air; but there was no air. Only smoke, choking smoke.

The screams and the shouts and the thunder seemed not so near now. Everything was farther away. He was alone in the darkness, choking, choking.

He tried to shout, but there was only a pitiful rasping gurgle in his throat. He goaded his dulled mind, seeking an explanation. He found one.

"The trial is over," he told himself calmly. "The trial is over, and I was pronounced guilty. I am no longer in the cell. The smoke and heat have dulled my wits. I am at the stake, and I am burning. Why is everything so dark? Perhaps my eyes were the first to suffer. Well, then, this is the end of Kieron-head-in-the-air. It is not so bad as I thought."

He fell down, groping on the cell floor, coughing monstrously, but still conscious. "I am in my cell," he told himself. "I am in my cell. No. It is an illusion."

The stones of the cell floor were warm. He felt them against his face. "It is an illusion. It must be an illusion. The dying man seeks to escape his fate. What a pity I cannot tell —"

He slumped unconscious.

Outside his cell, out in the streets of Arundel, the screaming and the shouting and the banging and the burning continued. But, mercifully, Kieron was oblivious of it all. He lay on the cell floor, his open mouth touching the stone, his lungs still pitifully striving to suck in what little air remained. He was like to have choked on the smoke, had not two things happened in rapid succession. A wild, bearded, blood-stained man with an axe battered down the smouldering door and thrust a blazing torch through the doorway so that he could see if the room contained anything of value. The torch flickered and died for lack of air; but before it died, the intruder was able to discern what appeared to be a dead man on the floor. Coughing and spluttering and cursing, the bearded man retreated. A corpse did not merit his attention.

Shortly after that, the wind changed, and the smoke was drawn out of the cell.

Kieron had been near to death; and it was many hours before he returned to conscious life.

There were blisters on his hands and feet and face. The pain was abominable. Every movement he made caused him to cough excrutiatingly. But, somehow, he dragged himself to his feet and staggered out of the cell, out of the House of Correction. He trod, unheeding, on the body of Brother Sebastian. Brother Sebastian's throat had been cut. But Kieron did not notice.

It was shortly after daybreak.

He went out into the streets of Arundel.

It was a dead town. Dead, with the wreckage of its houses still smouldering. Apart from the crash of falling timbers, the crackle and spitting of charred wood, there was no sound. No sound of humanity. Arundel was deserted by the living, and the dead lay where they had fallen.

The nightmare that had followed the dreams was real.

Part Two

AIRBORNE

I

HIS CONSCIOUS MIND numbed by shock, and like one who had taken too much strong spirit, Kieron lurched towards the castle. The main gate hung in fragments, destroyed, apparently, by some explosion.

He clambered over the remains of the gate and the corpses of the men who had tried to defend it. His mind refused to work. He tried to think. But his mind simply refused to work.

He followed his instincts only. And his instincts led him to seek out Alyx.

He found her.

And then he wished he had not found her.

She lay in the great hall, below the minstrel gallery. She lay on the floor of the great hall with her nightdress flung over her head and her legs wide apart. She lay with a sword that had passed through her navel pinning her to the wooden floor.

Kieron inflicted on himself the supreme punishment. He drew back her nightdress and looked upon her face. A pale, bruised stranger was revealed, her eyes wide with a horror now beginning to glaze in death, her mouth now open and slack, and the blood dried upon lips that she had bitten in her torment.

Kieron was man enough to understand the terrible fashion of her death, and boy enough to be shattered by grief. Letting out a great cry of anguish, he fell to his knees, and stooped to kiss the cold forehead. His tears fell upon her face and, half-crazed with grief and horror, it seemed to him that she wept also.

"Alyx! Alyx!" he sobbed. "Would that I lay dead with you." Then another thought pricked through his anguish, pricking deep like the thrust of a sword. "No, by the hammer of Ludd, I will stay alive and seek those who have done this thing. And, if I find them, I will find a means to inflict a terrible punishment, or I will perish. This I swear." Then he closed her eyes gently and eased the sword out of her body. It had a narrow blade. No blood came.

"I will keep this sword," he said aloud, "to return to those who have left it." He straightened Alyx Fitzalan's limbs, smoothed her nightdress down decently over the outraged body. Then he stroked her hair a while. Presently, he murmured: "Rest quiet now, my dear one. I must look to the living; though the dead shall never be forgot."

Sword in hand, he moved cautiously through the castle. The devastation and carnage appalled him. Many of Seigneur Fitzalan's men lay dead, with weapons in their hands. Many strangers, also. Strangers in strange clothes, with black skins, white skins and brown.

Of the two younger Fitzalan daughters there was nothing to be seen. Perhaps they had been taken away, or had been killed elsewhere. Seigneur Fitzalan himself, Kieron soon discovered in one of the upper corridors. He lay on the floor, outside a chamber door, sword in one hand, dagger in the other, and with a great red stain on the fine linen that covered his breast, and a look of profound astonishment frozen on his face.

Inside the chamber, on a larger bed than Kieron had ever before seen, a bed whose fine silk coverings were now bloody and torn, lay the seigneur's lady. Her clothes had been ripped from her; and, by the look of it, she had suffered as Alyx had suffered, perhaps even more horribly.

Kieron could not bear to look long, could not even bear to decently enshroud the dead woman. He had had his fill of terror. He stumbled from the room, feeling foul juices rise from his stomach to his dry mouth. He was sick in the corridor, but there was none to remark his weakness.

After he had vomited, his head felt more clear. He felt better altogether. Weak, but definitely better. He began to think. The devastation was terrible. Arundel and its castle had been laid waste; but not everyone could have been killed. Some must have fled to the downs; and the downs folk themselves — including his father and mother — should have had ample warning of the attack. With luck, there would be many who had escaped the night of madness. He must find them. He must find his own people, and learn the nature of the catastrophe and what could be done about it.

Sword in hand, Kieron wandered down long, dark passageways, dully seeking his way out of the castle.

He heard a sound, a deep groaning. He stopped and listened. The groaning came again. He went towards it.

The sound led him back to the great hall. Not far from where Alyx lay, a stranger lay also, dressed in outlandish clothes. There was much blood upon his stomach, the evidence of good sword thrusts. Kieron could not understand why he had not noticed him before.

The stranger had brown skin, and eyes that rolled horribly. He mumbled something in a language that Kieron could not understand. His fingers fluttered, as if in supplication.

It came to Kieron, as he regarded the man, that he might well have been one of those who had outraged Alyx.

Kieron was glad of the thought. Here, at last, was someone from whom he could extract vengeance.

He raised the sword that he held, the sword that had transfixed Alyx.

"May Ludd have mercy upon you," said Kieron. "I will not."

He thrust the sword home, once, twice, three times.

The brown-faced man grunted with each thrust. Then he uttered a great sigh and died.

113

Kieron exalted in his death. One blow for Alyx.

Then, hardly knowing where he was going or what he was doing, he somehow found his way out of the castle.

He was amazed to notice that it was a day of bright sunlight. Alyx and her parents lay dead in the castle, towns folk lay butchered in the streets and the remains of houses still smouldered. He gazed up at the blue sky incredulously and shielded his eyes from the glare. The sun was wrong. It should not have been a day for sunlight.

He tried to think what to do now. He must try to find Gerard and Kristen, anyone at all who remained alive. He must try to discover what had happened.

Wearily, still clutching the sword, he staggered away from the castle towards the downs. There had to be people left alive among the hills. Not everyone could have been killed.

He felt dreadfully thirsty. His throat was raw and sore, his lips blistered. Not fifty paces from the castle, he gave a despairing cry and fell on his face.

There had been sunlight, and now darkness was closing in. He was glad of the darkness. It came as a friend.

Kieron was near to his eighteenth birthday, the threshhold of manhood; but the events of the last few hours had aged him greatly. Already he had seen much. More than a grown man might be expected to witness and yet retain his reason.

Kieron took refuge in the friendly darkness. It lay over him like a blanket of peace.

2

SHOLTO POURED WATER between his lips. Petrina held his head. Someone was trying to take the sword from his hand but his fingers would not let go.

"Peace, boy," said Sholto. "You are safe. I have carried you on my back with that sword like to pierce my foot at every step. Let it go now. You are with friends."

Kieron sat up, blinked his eyes, licked his lips, trying to comprehend where he was and what was happening. Petrina kissed him, and he let her take the sword from his hand. His fingers ached — how they ached! He must have been gripping the sword very tightly.

He looked around him. He was in a woodland clearing, presumably in the downs. The sun was still high. There were many people in the clearing: downs folk and towns folk. Strangers and friends. He did not see his parents.

"My father and mother?" They were his first words. He did not like the sound of his voice. It was rasping, shaky, like that of an old man. The smoke was still in his lungs. It made him cough when he spoke.

"Rest easy, lad," said Sholto. "There are misfortunes that must be borne."

"Dead?"

"Ay, dead . . . Your father gave a good accounting. We found three dead men who would not dispute the claim."

"My mother?"

Sholto said gently: "My son, forgive me. There are things for which I cannot find the words. I am a simple man. Forgive me. Also, my own wife is dead, and my mind is not too clear ... Your mother was a woman of great presence. She is dead. Let us say no more."

Kieron digested this information. Sholto was right, he thought dully. Better not to enquire further.

Petrina said: "Kieron, thank Ludd you are alive."

"Alyx Fitzalan is dead," he said. "The sword you took from my hand is the one I plucked from her belly."

Petrina kissed him once more. "Ludd rest her. She was beautiful. I have no quarrel with the spirit of Mistress Fitzalan."

"Well, then," said Kieron, his voice rising. "Who has destroyed us? What manner of men are they who came to destroy and pillage and ravish in the night?"

A strange face loomed before him. "Sir, they are free-booters, scavengers, parasites. They came from the coast of North Africa. They have worked the Mediterranean coasts dry. Now they venture into Europe."

Kieron looked up and saw a gaunt wild-eyed man in ragged clothes. A patch of blood showed through the rags on his shoulder. His weathered face and something about his manner suggested that he was a seaman.

"How do you know these things?"

"I have sailed with them."

Automatically, Kieron felt for his sword. "You have sailed with them!" He leaped to his feet. "Then —"

"Peace, boy," said Sholto. "I do not wish to knock your head. The stranger comes as a friend."

"I did not sail willingly. I was taken for a slave."

"They take slaves?" Kieron was utterly appalled.

"Both male and female," said the man sombrely. "When the slave is strong and well, he is given food. When he falls ill or is no longer of use, he is thrown overboard. So, also, is it with women."

"They cannot be human!"

The stranger gave a wintry smile. "Human they may not be, but they are mortal. I have had little pleasure this past year; but one I savour is that I twisted chains about the necks of two of those who had set chains upon my wrists and ankles. Look, sir. It gave me pleasure to tear the flesh from my wrists so that two might die."

He held out his arms. Kieron looked at the bloody mess on his wrists and turned away.

"I struck off the chains myself," said Sholto.

When he had recovered himself, Kieron turned to the stranger. "I ask your pardon, sir."

"No offence was given, sir. May the sword you have taken have some further acquaintance with those who brought it."

"Ludd be willing," said Sholto.

Kieron gathered his wits and looked round the clearing. There were perhaps a hundred men, women and children gathered there. Some wore their night clothes, some were injured, some sat silently or wept, some carried arms and strolled about nervously, unable to keep still.

"Are these all who have lived through it?" asked Kieron.

"No, boy, there are many more. Our numbers grow, as you see." He pointed to a group of five people who had just arrived. "Most of the downs folk were untouched. We have sent messengers, telling them to rally here at the Misery."

Suddenly, Kieron recollected where he was. The Misery was a high stretch of woodland about five kilometres from Arundel. As children, he and Petrina had played in the Misery, marvelling at its name, marvelling at its huge beech trees. There was a day, long ago, when they had lain under a beech and listened to the song of the bees, when Petrina had told him of the predictions of the astrologer Marcus, and when he had confessed to her his desire to fly.

But all that was far away in a world of children, a world long dead.

"Why do you send for people to rally here?"

"Why else," said Sholto, "except that when our numbers are strong we should venture down to the sea at

Little Hampton, where the invaders now lie, and give them a taste of their own physic."

Kieron left Sholto and Petrina, and sought out the stranger with bloody wrists.

"How many ships have they?"

"Ten, perhaps twelve now. More will be coming."

"How many men?"

The stranger shrugged. "Eight hundred, a thousand. More will be coming."

"How many more?"

"Who can say? They are a nation which thrives upon the misfortunes of other nations. They are the people of the sea. They have no home. They settle like locusts. And, like locusts, when the food is gone, they go elsewhere."

"You say they are a nation. How can they be a nation? I have seen some of their dead. They are of different colours, different races."

"They have one thing in common. They are all men without a country. Each has forfeited the right to live at peace in the land of his birth. They are all the more dangerous because they have put themselves beyond the acceptance of civilised men. They have little to lose. They call themselves the Brotherhood of Death."

Petrina tugged at Kieron's arm. "Come and take some food, Kieron. You must need it. When did you last eat?"

He tried to remember. Yesterday, he must have eaten. But yesterday was more than a few hours ago. Yesterday was a lost world. He tried to remember when he had eaten and what he had eaten. He could not.

Petrina led him near to a fire over which a large cauldron bubbled. She gave him a platter filled with stew. He sat down cross-legged, and ate mechanically. His brain told him that the stew contained rabbit and parsnips and carrots and potatoes and herbs. It tasted like wet sand.

People continued to arrive at the Misery. One of them was Aylwin. He was in a poor condition, half fainting. He had been supported on the journey by his mother, Lilias. When she had seen him safely received, she went away from the Misery and plunged a dagger into her heart. Her husband was dead, and she had received much attention from the Brotherhood of Death. She no longer wished to live.

"Aylwin!" said Kieron. "I am glad to see you alive."

Aylwin held out his right arm. "Be not too glad, Kieron. The world we knew has gone for ever." There was a tight rope round his wrist, where the hand had been severed. "I will paint no more."

"You will paint again," said Kieron. "This I swear."

Brothers Hildebrand and Lemuel came to attend to Aylwin.

Kieron looked at them scornfully. "You seek a hot-air balloon, brothers? I have not had time to construct another. And where is Brother Sebastian, that devout scourge of heretics?"

"Brother Sebastian is dead," said Lemuel mildly.

"Aha The Divine Boy was impatient for his company."

Hildebrand held out his hand. "Peace, Kieron. What is past is past. Brother Sebastian was, perhaps, over-zealous. There will be no reckoning."

"Peace, you say! A strange word when the seigneur and his family lie horribly dead, and half the towns folk with them. By the hammer of Ludd, there will be a reckoning, Brother. But it will not be for a hot-air balloon."

Petrina scolded him. "Speak no more, Kieron. Bitter words are not needed on this day of grief. The brothers have used their skills upon the sick and wounded, also they have hazarded their lives more than once." She put her arm round Aylwin who was near to fainting. "Would you make speeches while Aylwin bleeds to death?"

"Forgive me," said Kieron. "As always, I am a fool. I will not unsay what I have said, but let us wipe the slate."

"Kieron," said Hildebrand, "you speak plain. The slate is clean. All of us now need each other. Perhaps that is the divine purpose."

The neddies took Aylwin away and made a rough

couch for him of grass and bracken. Presently, Kieron heard him moaning; and then the moaning rose to a screaming. Kieron stood up and tried to go to his friend. But there was no strength in his legs, and the world had begun to spin crazily, and Petrina was saying words that he could not hear.

And then there was nothing but nightmares. And when he woke he could still hear screaming, but the voice was his own.

3

FOR HUNDREDS OF years in the island of Britain there
had been no monarchy, no parliament, no central authority.
The country had been divided into seigneuries, each held
and governed feudally. The grand seigneurs, the largest
land-owners, occasionally held counsel in London. Their
concerns were largely with matters of agriculture and
trade. They were not empowered to raise taxes, establish
armies, or decide matters of national policy. Each seigneur
was responsible for the security of his own domain. He
could, and frequently did, seek alliance one way or another
with his neighbours; and by means of intermarriage,
many seigneuries were enlarged or united with others. It
had been the intent of Fitzalan of Arundel to bring his
seigneurie and that of Talbot of Chichester together by
marriage. Besides, since Talbot was unlikely to last, the
seigneuries might have united in a manner most satisfactory to the Fitzalans. But Fate had put paid to that;
and the dream of an enlarged and prosperous seigneurie
had perished with the deaths of Fitzalan and his daughter.

Though there was no centre of temporal authority in
Britain, there was yet a centre of spiritual authority: the
Luddite Church. The First and Second Men having been
destroyed, as it were, by their own hands in the manner
of their indiscriminate use of machines, Luddism developed from an almost forgotten philosophy of un-
tutored men into a flourishing creed. Ned Ludd, the idiot
boy, who took a hammer to destroy weaving machines at
the beginning of the Industrial Revolution, slowly assumed
the mantle of divinity.

As Christianity declined, so Luddism rose. It was a more appropriate philosophy. Jesus of Nazareth, or Joshua ben David, to give him his proper Hebrew name, had never had to consider the moral problems involved in the use of machines. Chiefly, he had spoken for universal brotherhood, and he had spoken against oppression. His philosophies were outmoded. More important than universal brotherhood and oppression was the question of survival of the human race. Twice the human race had attempted to destroy itself by the use of machines. In retrospect, it was seen that the one person who had opposed machines was the true saviour of mankind. Ned Ludd, the idiot boy of Leicestershire, acquired in retrospect divine power. It was discovered that he had broken small loaves and fed thousands. It was discovered that he had walked upon the river Trent without sinking. It was discovered that he had changed water into beer, on the eve of his crucifixion.

So, in Britain, the Luddite Church waxed strong; and anti-machinism grew into a religion powerful enough to inhibit all forms of invention. Powerful enough to compel the seigneurs to accept that any unauthorised machinery was evil.

The Luddite Church was peculiar to Britain; but the revulsion for machines was universal. Throughout the world, as men struggled to emerge from the centuries of barbarism that had followed the destruction of the second machine-based civilisation, there lingered an almost racial dread of the power of machines. In some races and in some countries it was stronger than in others. In Russia and China and Africa and India, where a machine-based way of living had never been fully accepted by the mass of the people, the people had, for the most part, returned to the ways of their long dead ancestors. They ploughed the land with wooden ploughs drawn by oxen, mules, horses. They threshed their corn or rice with flails. They killed game with spears or arrows. They used spinning-wheels and wove cloth laboriously by hand.

But in Japan, where the dread of machines was accompanied by a fatal fascination, the steam-engine had been developed once more, and men were already experimenting with its use to propel vehicles and small boats. The Japanese, however, had turned once more to their historic philosophy of isolation; and Japanese steam-engines were retained only for the domestic use of the Japanese.

The steam-engine had also been reintroduced to the continent of North America; but there it was being used primarily in the tremendous task of re-establishing transcontinental communication. It would be many years yet before American ships, powered by steam, proved more efficient in crossing the Atlantic Ocean than the great windjammers.

Meanwhile, the Luddite Church of Britain, an island which had once been the cradle of a great Industrial Revolution, authoritatively maintained that all unnecessary machines — that is, machines considered by the Church to be unnecessary — were evil. And so Britain was condemned to remain one of the most backward countries of Europe.

But the coming of the freebooters, who had attacked along the south coast not only near Arundel but in many other places, eventually provided Kieron with the opportunity to weaken the hold that the Luddite Church had over the minds of men, and to demonstrate that machines, which had enabled two civilisations to be destroyed, were also necessary for the survival and advancement of a third.

4

KIERON SLEPT THROUGHOUT the rest of the day and the
following night, while downs folk and people from
the farther parts of the seigneurie continued to arrive at the
Misery, alerted by messengers who rode the downs on
horseback. Fortunately, the weather remained mild and
dry. The able-bodied men set about building rough huts
and tents; some of them hunted for deer, rabbit, pheasant;
the women prepared food and attended to the injured.

Kieron did not return to consciousness when Sholto
lifted him bodily and carried him to a small shelter made
of spruce branches and bracken. Nor was he aware that
Petrina sat with him through the night, soothing him,
cooling his hot forehead, murmuring words of tenderness
when he cried out.

In the early morning, he awoke refreshed, his head
marvellously clear. He ate pheasant breast and drank
goat's milk at sunrise, and he began to feel a new man.
Apart from posted watchmen, hardly anyone in the camp
was stirring. They were all tired from shock, or wounds
or various exertions. When he had breakfasted, he drew
Petrina back into the shelter. She was exhausted from a
night of sleeplessness, but Kieron did not know this. He
unbuttoned her blouse and fondled her breasts. Petrina
moaned with pleasure, her fatigue forgotten. The sound
of her voice and the feel of her breasts excited him beyond
endurance. He lay with her. It was a necessity. He lay
with her. It was the first time he had lain with a woman.

He wondered why it had been so necessary. It was more
than simple desire, he thought hazily. It was, he sup-

posed, an affirmation of love and life. He had seen much death and much horror. Now he had sought refuge from it in physical and emotional union. He remembered Alyx. He remembered Alyx with love. It was no disloyalty to Petrina. He remembered the Alyx of *Mistress Fitzalan's Leap*. That was best way to remember her. The rest was nightmare . . .

Afterwards, he and Petrina lay close, whispering, sharing. Someday, he would tell her about Alyx; and someday, she, too, would share the mourning. And together they would pick flowers in remembrance . . .

Presently, the camp in the Misery — so appropriately named — became alive with activity. Women prepared hot food. Men looked to their weapons, consulted with each other, enquired of the latest news. Kentigern, Seigneur Fitzalan's bailiff, had somehow managed to escape the destruction at the castle with nothing more than flesh-wounds in the leg and shoulder. In the absence of higher authority, Kentigern was considered by common consent to be the leader of the survivors. He was a capable man. Already, he had sent messengers to London to acquaint the Grand Council with the state of affairs. And he had sent men both east and west to ascertain the extent of the freebooters' invasion.

The stranger who had sailed with the freebooters was called Isidor. Once he had been mate on a four-masted barque plying along the European coast for the wine trade. His vessel had been taken by the freebooters off the coast of Spain with many casks of wine on board. The captain was hanged and the crew enslaved. Many of them had subsequently died of fevers and poor rations. Isidor was one of the last survivors.

While Kentigern awaited the results of his communications, and while more people congregated in the Misery, Kieron sought information from Isidor. He wanted to know more about the freebooters.

For more than a hundred years, so Isidor told him, the freebooters had been a pestilence in the Mediterranean

Ocean. Though they were drawn from many countries and many creeds, they had these things in common: that each had put himself outside the law in the land of his birth, and that each had little liking for honest toil. For many years, though their acts of violence and theft had been terrible to those who had to endure them, the free-booters had not constituted a serious threat to the security of nations. They had sailed only in small groups consisting of two, perhaps three or four, vessels, despoiling only isolated communities and occupying captured territory only for so long as it took to organise a force sufficient to repel them. Frequently, when their strength was challenged, they would put to sea without giving battle. Their strength had lain in their very elusiveness.

But, of recent years, their numbers had grown, and their strength had increased in an alarming fashion. They had become unified under the absolute command of a man who styled himself Admiral Death. No one knew his real name. No one knew from which country he came, for he spoke many languages, as if to the manner born.

Admiral Death, according to Isidor, was still a young man, perhaps not yet thirty years old. Yet he had natural authority, the gift of commanding. In the space of a few years he had unified the numerous small groups of Mediterranean freebooters. He had transformed them into a sea-borne nation, subject to its own laws, acknowledging the sovereignty of no other nation upon earth. Every man and woman in the freebooters had sworn absolute allegiance to him. His word was life or death.

He held some curious notions. He would not tolerate children or pregnant women. Children, wherever he found them, were put to the sword. Women who were demonstrably pregnant when captured were likewise put to the sword. If they became pregnant later, they were thrown overboard. Clearly, Admiral Death had little interest in man's greatest hope of immortality.

His flag ship, from which Isidor had escaped, now lay anchored off Little Hampton. It was Admiral Death who had personally led the thrust inland to Arundel. It was Admiral Death who had devised the concerted attacks along the south coast of Britain.

According to Isidor, it was Admiral Death's intention to establish a semi-permanent colony on the shores of Britain, from which he would be able to conduct his attacks along the northern coasts of Europe. Ironically, he had chosen Britain because of the strength of the Luddite Church. He knew that the Luddites held machines to be anathema. Consequently, he knew also that the ability of the people on the island of Britain to defend themselves would be severely restricted. Admiral Death was a great believer in machines. He had much experience of their usefulness — in a purely destructive sense. He had the use of gunpowder and cannon; and his engineers had devised siege engines — ballistae and the like — capable of hurling explosive bombs against fortified positions. Admiral Death did not despise swords, bows, axes and crossbows; but he knew from experience that they were no match for bombshell and cannon. The god of war smiled not upon the righteous but upon superiority of weapons.

Admiral Death, however, had one major weakness. It was a weakness common to all seafaring men. He was afraid of fire. But he was more than ordinarily afraid. He was unreasonably afraid. It was said that some years ago he had been plundering a Mediterranean French city and had been accidentally trapped in a waterfront warehouse when one of his men put it to the torch. It was said that, though Admiral Death eventually managed to escape, he had been severely burned, particularly about his legs, and that his manhood was gone from him for ever.

Kieron, who had been listening to Isidor gloomily, brightened at this latest intelligence.

"You have spoken with Kentigern of these matters?"

"Ay, that I have. He has heard what you have heard and more."

"Then our task is clear. We must prey upon this

madman's fears. We must fire his ships and inflict such damage that, to his dying day — which, Ludd permitting, may be soon — he will have cause to regret that he came to these shores."

Isidor smiled. "Easily said, my friend. Because of his fear, the Admiral is doubly cautious. Such vessels as now lie tied up at Little Hampton are well protected. Other vessels lie out at anchor. Strict watch is kept. It will be hard to surprise them."

"We shall find a way," said Kieron. "We shall find a way. To know the enemy's true weakness is surely half the battle."

5

KENTIGERN HAD BEEN a good bailiff, but he was not a
good general. Now that Seigneur Fitzalan and his family
were dead, Kentigern was regarded as the temporary
leader of those who had survived, until Seigneur Fitzalan's
closest surviving relative laid claim to the lands and
properties of the seigneurie. It therefore fell to Kentigern
to determine how and when and if the forces of Admiral
Death should be attacked and repulsed.

Several hundred people had now rallied to the Misery.
There were many women and children; but also there
were two hundred or more men capable of bearing arms.
Kentigern's first thought was to send a sortie into Arundel
to discover if the invaders had maintained any presence
there and also to list the extent of the damage suffered by
the town.

He did not wish to risk many of his fighting force. So
he called for twenty volunteers. Among those who stood
forward and received his approval were Kieron, Sholto
and Isidor.

The twenty men approached Arundel with great caution. They carried swords, bows, crossbows, clubs. Their
caution was unjustified. They found Arundel as Kieron
had last seen it — deserted, except by the dead. Evidently,
Admiral Death's men had retired to Little Hampton, there
to consolidate their defences.

The party was led by Kentigern's second-in-command,
a man called Liam who had once been a captain of
foot soldiers and had some skill in the art of fighting.
When Liam had assured himself that none living remained

in Arundel, he was of a mind to return to the Misery and report his findings to Kentigern. But Kieron spoke with him.

It was a fine, bright day, but chilly. Sea birds had come inland. They pecked at corpses in the streets, and scratched and squabbled amid the desolation.

"Master Liam, should we not bury our dead?" asked Kieron.

Liam gazed about him hopelessly. "I am commanded to report upon the state of the town and the castle, Kieron. Besides, we are but twenty men. It would take us more than two days to bury those who have fallen."

"Must we leave them to the sea birds and the weather?" demanded Sholto. "I think not, captain. These were our folk. I will dig all day and all night, if need be. I am a strong man, and I will undertake to dig deep enough to bury twenty myself."

Kieron thought for a moment. "Liam is right, Sholto. We would exhaust ourselves trying to bury all the dead. We shall need our strength to avenge them ... But suppose we collected the bodies. Suppose we burned them, perhaps in the castle yard. At least, we would save them from the sea birds; and there are enough of us to make our farewells to them in a civilised fashion."

"The invaders would see the smoke," objected Liam. "They might think that we have returned to our homes, and be tempted to make a second attack."

"It would take them more than an hour to march inland from the coast," Kieron pointed out. "When they first came, we were unprepared, expecting no attack. Men, women and children were butchered defenceless in the night. But if they came again, though there are not many of us, we are armed and ready. We know this country, and they do not. If we light the funeral pyre in the late afternoon, and if these freebooters march upon us, we can inflict much damage before we retire. It would be something to dispatch a score or two of murderers at the funeral of our friends."

"That is good reasoning," commented Isidor. "If they do not come, we have no difficulties. If they do come, we can kill a few before we retreat into the darkness."

Liam scratched his head. "Kentigern asked only for news. He gave no instruction as to the dead."

"Kentigern has much on his mind," observed Kieron mildly. "His concern is rightly with the living. But he is not a hard man. If he were here, I believe he would allow us to take care of our dead. He would not wish to see them reduced to carrion."

Liam made up his mind. "By the hammer, you are right, boy. Therefore, let us prepare a large bed of wood, which is all we can now offer these who were our friends."

There was plenty of wood available. Large stocks of logs were always in store at the castle. Also much half-burned timber lay around for the picking up. Presently, a very large platform of wood had been established in the castle yard. It was broad enough and long enough to support many bodies; and it rose almost the height of a man's shoulders from the ground.

Now came the more arduous and less pleasant task: the collecting of the bodies. Kieron, Sholto and two other men elected to gather the dead from the castle and its grounds. The remaining men split themselves into three groups and took hand carts to scour the town.

There was one body that Kieron wished to deal with himself, alone; though he knew that it would break his heart.

Alyx lay as he had left her, undisturbed. But she now bore little resemblance to the Alyx Fitzalan who had once been so full of life and love and sheer grace. The body was a pale, shrunken thing, grotesque, doll-like.

The tears coursed down Kieron's face. He forced himself to look so that the manner of her death would be burned into his brain for ever. There were the lips he had kissed. There were the breasts that had been held warmly against him.

"Alyx, dear and lovely Alyx," he sobbed. "I will kill for you. If need be, I will spend my life killing for you, until the last of the animals who brought you to this has perished horribly, and the earth is clean."

He found some torn brocade hanging by a window, and wrapped her carefully. It was Indian cloth of gold and silver, a fitting shroud for a child of sunlight and movement.

And when she was covered, all of her, he held her close for the last time. And as held her, he saw the picture: *Mistress Fitzalan's Leap*. He marvelled that he had not noticed it before — his first and last painting. It hung crazily from the wall, and had been slashed by a sword. But the damage was not irreparable. The canvas could be sewn, and fresh pigments would conceal the joining.

Kieron knew that he could never paint like that again. It did not matter. The Alyx who lay in his arms was dead. But the Alyx of the portrait was alive in all the bloom and exuberance of youth. That was how she must now live, he told himself bitterly, caught like a fly in amber. When there was time, he would attend to the portrait; and a hundred years hence men would marvel at her grace and beauty.

He lifted his burden and carried it out to the funeral pyre. The men had worked hard at their grim task. Already, the bodies were piled high. Kieron climbed on to the pyre, treading carefully so that he would not disturb the dead, and laid Alyx as near as he could to the body of her father.

When he came down, Sholto and the others spoke to him, but he did not hear what they were saying.

Men were sprinkling whale oil on the timbers. Presently all was ready.

"Will someone say something?" asked Liam.

"I will say something." Kieron suddenly recollected what was happening. "I will say something. Before the torch is put to this pyre which will consume the remains of our loved ones and friends, I ask that all here will swear to take ten lives for one or to die in their efforts. We deal not with people but with animals. We deal with the instruments of death."

"It is a beautiful oath," said Isidor. "I swear."

"I also," said Sholto, "though Ludd knows we are not a fighting people."

The fire leaped high, and the men drew back from the heat, staring as if in a trance as the logs and timbers spit and cracked, and the flames roared like living creatures in the light wind.

Liam had sent a man up to the watch tower to keep an eye on the river and the road to the sea and the flat coastal land; but the rest of the men stayed in the castle yard, held almost magically by the great wall of fire that now rose up to surround and consume the dead.

The heat grew intense, and the men had to stand farther and farther back, while their faces became red and the sweat dried as it was formed.

Great gouts of black smoke rose to the sky, sparks showered; and the fire of death roared with its own self-consuming life.

"Farewell for ever," said Kieron silently. "If there is a life hereafter, as the neddies swear, may you again ride a fine horse, Alyx, on a June morning. And presently I will join you and paint such a picture of you held between earth and sky that all the ghosts of all the men who ever lived will marvel. But, forgive me, I think that life is only for the living; and so your final refuge is in the memories of those who have known and loved you."

The man who had been in the watch tower was speaking excitedly to Liam. Kieron emerged from his private thoughts to learn that, in the fading light, the watch man had seen a column of men marching from Little Hampton. He estimated that they would reach the castle within the half-hour.

"If we are prudent," said Liam, "we will shortly depart from this place. We have fulfilled our task and more.

We have seen to our dead, and we may retire with honour."

"Not I!" shouted Kieron wildly. "I mourn my dead, and I am anxious to demand a reckoning."

Liam, a strong man, seized him by the shoulders and shook him. "Boy, your spirit is great, but you are half crazed with grief. We are twenty men. I am told a hundred or more march against us. They have weapons at the very least equal to ours and possibly superior. Now is not the time to fulfil your oath. Be patient. The time will come when we may strike."

Kieron broke his hold. "Sir, you are a good man, and you lead us. As you say, I am half crazed with grief. But grief sharpens my wits. These who march against us will have to come up the hill to the castle, will they not?"

"So?"

"So, we have burned our dead. May we not offer a similar accommodation to the freebooters? I am told that Admiral Death has little liking for fire."

"You speak in riddles, Kieron. Speak plain before we depart, taking you forcibly, if need be."

Kieron tried to accommodate his thoughts. "They come against us, these freebooters, drawn by the sight of the funeral pyre. In the castle cellars there will doubtless still be many barrels of whale oil, along with logs and kindling. If we were to load four-wheel carts with the whale oil and with any substance that will burn, and if we were to wait until the freebooters were coming up the hill — "

Liam grasped the idea instantly. "Kieron, your thoughts have some greatness." He turned to the rest. "Sholto, take what men you need and find three four-wheel carts quickly. Mangan, take the rest of the men into the castle, bring out what is left of the whale oil and any substance that will burn quickly."

Presently, the carts were loaded with barrels of oil, small wood, cloth and straw, and anything that would burn quickly. Then they were hauled out of the castle gate to the top of the hill, and were ready for launching down the road to the sea.

The watch man reported that the freebooters were already crossing the bridge over the river Arun. Twilight came rapidly. It was hard to see down the length of the hill from the castle gate.

"If the ruse does not work," said Liam, "we shall have to run for our lives. We cannot stand against so many."

"It will work," said Kieron with utter confidence. "The darkness comes fast, but that is no matter. Indeed it is to our advantage. We know their numbers, they do not know ours. In the darkness, and with chariots of fire bursting upon them, they will panic. Such as escape burning, we may easily put to the sword. Let us listen for their feet and their voices before we launch the attack. Let us hear their breathing."

Liam looked at him with respect. "Some day, you may be a great general, Kieron."

Kieron laughed. "Some day, I shall be a general of the clouds."

The freebooters began to ascend the hill. The darkness made the shape of their column indistinct; but their voices and the clatter of their arms could be heard clearly. They marched without any attempt at concealment, without any sign of fear. What was there to be afraid of? The inhabitants of this town were largely dead or taken prisoner. The survivors could only be a cowed and desperate few.

Now they were less than a hundred paces from the castle gate. Now they were no more than sixty or seventy paces away. Their faces began to show ruddily in the reflected glow of the funeral pyre.

"Now!" shouted Liam.

Three men flung torches on to heaps of cloth and straw soaked in whale oil. The rest pushed at the wheels and sent the carts careering down the hill.

Within moments, the flames rose high. Burning whale

oil slopped from the barrels and on to the wheels, turning the carts truly into chariots of fire. The freebooters were confronted with a fearsome sight. The fire-carts bearing down upon them took up most of the width of the narrow street. In the terrible moments as the carts gathered speed, the column of freebooters panicked, became an unreasoning mob. The front ranks turned to flee, elbowing and kicking their fellows out of the way, trampling some of them. But the fire-carts were already moving faster than a man could run.

Four or five of the freebooters retained cool heads and pressed themselves against the castle walls to allow the fire-carts to run past. It availed them little. They fell to arrows from bows or bolts from crossbows, their positions being made wonderfully clear by the light from the flames.

Two of the carts collided and careened crazily. Their flaming barrels of whale oil shattered upon the street, creating a terrible river of fire. Men danced dreadfully in it as their legs burned, or fell into it and were destroyed with merciful speed.

The carnage was horrible, but it lasted no more than two minutes. The carts reached the bottom of the steep hill and fell to pieces in great bursts of fire.

"We have worked a great destruction," said Liam. "Now let us go. This will be something to gladden the hearts of our people."

"Not I, captain. Not yet!" Kieron brandished the sword he had plucked from the body of Alyx. "There are those who still live. They are burned, but if we do not destroy them they will crawl back to their ships and they will live."

"Kieron reasons well, captain," said Sholto. "Let us — " He gave a great cough and looked at his chest in surprise. An arrow had buried itself deep. He sank to his knees. "Look after her," he said to Kieron. "But remember that a woman is — " He fell. Kieron knelt and lifted Sholto's head. But the smith's spirit had already departed his body.

"Well, then," said Kieron, standing up. "Who is for Sholto and those we have set upon the pyre this day?"

There was a great roar of approval. Liam sensed that it were better to go with the tide.

"Forward, then," said Kieron. "Kill without mercy." Nineteen men, armed with bows, swords and axes went down the hill.

The freebooters, such as survived, were in a pitiful condition. The river of fire had passed by them, round them, over them. They lay in the road, some dead, some still in great anguish, beating feebly at their smouldering clothes.

Kieron, dreadful to look at, his face distorted with anger, a torch in one hand and his sword in the other, leaped skilfully among the fiery rivulets of oil, the flaming wisps of straw and crackling fragments of timber.

He found one man, barely recognisable as a man, writhing. "One for Alyx!" The sword plunged into the freebooter's chest. He coughed, choked and lay still.

Another man, though badly burned, could still hold his sword. Pitifully, he tried to defend himself. But retribution was upon him.

"Another for Alyx!" Kieron was possessed.

He took joy in the killing. He leaped across islands of fire to seek out fresh victims.

"One more for Alyx!"

"A fourth for Alyx!"

One freebooter was not so badly burned that he could not go down on his knees and hold out his hands in an obvious appeal for mercy. He babbled in a tongue Kieron could not understand.

Kieron savoured the moment, dreadfully enjoying his power of life and death. "Mercy, you shall have, fellow. Better than your people gave." With a terrible sweep of the sword, he sliced through the freebooters's throat. The man fell, gurgling.

"Another for Alyx!" One small part of Kieron's mind remained shocked at the pleasure he could take in the death agony of a human being. The rest of him exulted in blood lust, goaded on by the vision of a girl who had been violated and brutally murdered.

He continued his deadly journey down the hill. With mindless fury, he struck at those who were already dying, even at some who were already dead. Presently he stopped, drained exhausted. There was no one left to kill.

He stared about him, as if in a trance. The flames were dying now. The battle, such as it had been, was over. More than a hundred corpses lay on the hill. The stench of burnt flesh was terrible and sweet.

He was aware that someone was shaking his shoulders. It was Liam.

"Kieron, are you well?"

Kieron looked at him vacantly. "Yes, captain, I am well."

"Listen, then. Your stratagem was wonderfully successful. But while you have been doing your bloody work, I have taken prisoners. They are not to be killed, Kieron. You understand? They are not to be killed."

"Why are they not to be killed?"

"Because they speak English. They will tell us more about Admiral Death, and his intentions."

"And when they have spoken?" asked Kieron.

"I do not know. It will be for Kentigern to decide."

"I have already decided," said Kieron, swaying. "It was my stratagem. They are my prisoners. The sentence is — " Suddenly, he fell, senseless. Liam picked him up and carried him back up the hill.

6

WITHIN THREE OR four days, the encampment in the Misery had become itself a small fortified village. Men had cut trees to build a stockade and to build kitchens and sleeping huts. Though the freebooters had evidently chosen not to occupy Arundel, Kentigern did not deem it safe to attempt to return to the town until his forces were stronger. He had barely two hundred men who could bear arms. Against the reputed strength of the forces of Admiral Death, they would have stood little chance in pitched battle.

Also Kentigern awaited news and instructions from the Grand Council of seigneurs in London, and from the east and the west concerning the extent of Admiral Death's invasion. The news was slow in coming; and when it came it was not overly encouraging. The grand seigneurs had had requests for help and guidance from the survivors in several seigneuries on or near the southern coast. But the grand seigneurs, besides being fortunate for the most part to hold lands at a reasonable distance from the coast, were prudent men. The forces of Admiral Death were highly mobile: the forces of the seigneuries were not. If sufficient men were committed to the south to repulse or defeat Admiral Death, what was to prevent him putting out to sea to strike at another vulnerable area of the coast? His ships could sail much faster than men could march or ride. If it were his pleasure, he could harry the entire coastline of the island of Britain, leaving its defenders to exhaust themselves marching to and fro in futile attempts to meet his invasions with strength.

So the Grand Council cautiously committed itself to raising a force of five hundred armed men within the month to march south, provided that the southern seigneuries affected by the invasion could establish a unified army which at least doubled the strength of the Grand Council's auxiliaries. It was a diplomatic way of saying that the southern seigneuries must look to their own salvation.

The news from the east and the west was no less discouraging. A flotilla of Admiral Death's ships had struck with immense success as far east as the seigneurie of Brighton. Another had struck as far west as the seigneurie of Portsmouth. Each had advanced not inland but west and east respectively to join with the central assault at Little Hampton. Apparently, they were content to hold a long but narrow strip of coast.

The prisoners taken by Liam confirmed this interpretation — after they were put to the torture. The torture was not entirely barbaric. It consisted of tightening ropes about the arms and legs of the prisoners until pain loosened their tongues.

The most reliable informant was one Jethro, a favoured lieutenant of Admiral Death. His legs and arms had been already severely burned by Kieron's stratagem. The application of ropes served only to magnify a pain that already existed.

Jethro enlarged upon the information already received. Admiral Death had a grand design. He wished not only to establish a well-defended colony on the southern coast of Britain, but he wished also to use the island as a recruiting ground. If he was mad, he was also well-informed and concluded that many adventurous young men, tired of the restrictions and authoritarianism of the Luddites, would join his forces, attracted by the military and other machines that were denied them in the seigneuries. And if enough young malcontents did not come to him voluntarily, it would be easy to impress the men he needed by making punitive raids inland. He well knew that it would take the seigneurs a long time to unite in their common defence. Admiral Death did not require a long time for any of his operations. He was impatient of time. Soon he would be overwhelmingly strong, and whatever the seigneurs did then would not matter. Having consolidated his base, Admiral Death would then send ships to conduct similar operations along the coasts of Norway, Denmark, Germany and the Netherlands. Eventually he hoped to control the seaboard of Europe. When he had achieved this, he would be in a position to starve and weaken all who opposed him. And then he would be able to fulfil his great ambition — to make himself master of Europe.

Having disclosed his master's plans, Jethro pleaded movingly for his life, swearing that, upon recovery, he would willingly bear arms against the man to whom he had sworn loyalty. Kentigern, though short of seasoned fighters, reasoned that a man who broke fealty once might well do so again. He pronounced sentence of death.

Jethro was hanged on a fine morning when the birds sang and deer leaped through the woods. Kieron, present and assisting at the execution, saw the look in the fellow's eyes — the look of one who gazes upon the world for the last time and realises for the last time how beautiful it is. Briefly he felt pity; but then the pity dissolved in a dreadful vision of Alyx.

Because of his stratagem with the fire-carts, Kieron had become a hero among the survivors at the Misery. Men almost twice his age looked upon him with respect and listened to his ideas and opinions. He was no longer regarded as a heretic, one who had come close to the stake. All that seemed to belong to a world that had gone for ever. But his new status meant little to Kieron. He remained cold inside, cold with memories of cruelty and horror and death, cold with the knowledge of his own dreadful desire to seek vengeance.

Petrina noticed the change in him more than anyone.

On their fifth day at the Misery, they asked Brother Hildebrand to marry them. Their parents were dead, and they had no one left but each other. It seemed to Kieron a logical thing to do. He and Petrina would now be able to share the same bed and seek consolation in each other's arms without idle tongues wagging and without the censure of the neddies. Kieron went through the ceremony mechanically, his thoughts seeming to be far away. A special little hut had been prepared for them by friends, and a small and sadly gay feast had been arranged. But when Kieron and his bride retired to bed that night, he took no joy in her ample breasts and rounded belly. He performed his duty with the same remote efficiency he had displayed at the wedding. And Petrina was left to weep silently in the dark.

On the following day, Kentigern held a council of war. He was tired of waiting for help that did not come, he was tired of living in the woods like an outcast, he was tired of seeing people look to him for decisions and miracles.

Kieron, though young, was invited to attend the council because of his undoubted talent for destruction.

Kentigern spoke first. "Friends, you know what answer we have received from the grand seigneurs. They will help us, but it will take time; and they require us to establish an army consisting of all capable of bearing arms in the seigneuries that have already been attacked. That, too, will take time. I for one am unwilling to wait and see our people rot while such armies are gathered. Since the freebooters have shown no inclination to hold Arundel, it is possible for us to return to our homes and attempt to rebuild them. But, if we did, it is certain that our activities would be observed. Admiral Death, as we know, maintains a careful watch. At the first sign of our presence, no doubt he would send a force against us. We were not strong enough to resist the first attack. We would hardly be strong enough to resist a second. I propose, therefore, that we ourselves mount an attack upon his vessels at Little

Hampton. It will hardly be expected, and the element of surprise will surely afford us some advantage. I ask your opinions on these thoughts, my friends."

Some spoke for an attack, arguing that there was little to be lost and much to be gained. Some spoke against an attack, arguing that there was much to be lost and little to be gained. Kieron listened to all the speakers attentively, but did not himself offer an opinion.

Finally, Kentigern addressed him directly. "Well, Kieron, as I have observed, you have listened hard and said nothing. You have already proved yourself a man of some inspiration in the matter of inflicting losses upon the enemy. Have you nothing to say?"

Kieron smiled. "I am, as you know, one who desires to annihilate the freebooters utterly. My own plans would take time to put into action, assuming that you would be agreeable to them, which I doubt."

"Tell us of your plans, then, that we may judge."

"You know that I have experimented with a hot-air balloon?"

Kentigern shuffled uncomfortably. "Surely it is a thing best forgotten."

"No, Kentigern, it is a thing to remember. These facts are also things to remember. Admiral Death is afraid of fire. He commands the sea and he commands the land. He does not command the air. I desire to build a hot-air balloon capable of carrying two men. When the wind is right, this hot-air balloon would drift over the fleet at Little Hampton, raining fire upon the ships. Wooden ships will burn. If Admiral Death is deprived of his ships, he is also deprived of a means of supply and a means of retreat. Then would be the time to attack by land."

There were murmurs of shock and disapproval. Kieron's recent exploits had made him into a hero. Men did not wish to be reminded of matters that had brought him close to the stake.

Brother Hildebrand was among those present. "Kieron, my brother," he said mildly, "Ludd moves in mysterious ways, and has enabled you to redeem yourself in heroic action, of which Holy Church will take great notice. Do not, I beg of you, relapse into previous heresy."

"Will Holy Church send us one thousand soldiers?" demanded Kieron caustically. "Will the Divine Boy smash the ships of the freebooters with his divine hammer?"

"Peace," said Kentigern anxiously. "We are not gathered here to discuss doctrine or heresy. We are here to devise a means of ridding us of those who have fallen upon us like locusts. Will anyone else advise us?"

"Let us make use of Kieron's stratagem at the castle," said someone. "Let us by dead of night take small boats down the Arun. Let us take small boats loaded with casks of whale oil, straw and other combustibles. Let us tie them beneath the sterns of the freebooters' vessels and put them to the torch. Thus shall we inflict much damage."

"It will not work," said Kieron. "Their sentinels will be ready for us by sea, by river or by land. They cannot be ready for us by air."

"Nevertheless," said Kentigern, "the suggestion is a good one, and the best I have heard this day. I propose to commit one hundred men and ten fire-boats to this enterprise. It is my task now to seek volunteers, for I will not command men who have little enthusiasm for the venture."

Kieron was among the first to volunteer. Not because he had any faith in the venture, but because it might offer him another opportunity to kill freebooters.

The boats were launched into the Arun at night on the ebb. The Arun flowed swiftly, carrying the attacking party towards Little Hampton at better than five knots. For the major part of the journey, the men sat in the boats; but when they neared Little Hampton they slipped over the side and held on to the gunwales.

The water was icy cold, and many men had to bite hard on cloth or leather to stop their teeth chattering. Kentigern planned to let the boats drift, with the men hanging on to them, guiding them to the centre of the river. When Little

Hampton was reached, swimmers would attach the fire-boats to their target vessels and fuses would be ignited so that the boats would not burst into flame until the men had had at least some chance to make their escape.

The plan, as Kieron had foreseen, depended too heavily on an element of surprise which it would be hard to obtain. The drifting fire-boats were discovered before they reached Little Hampton. They were discovered by a small patrol of freebooters, equipped with lanterns, and marching along the bank of the river.

The boats were plainly visible by lantern light; and besides, one of Kentigern's men had sneezed. The free-booters began to use bows and muskets with terrible effect. The men in the water were too numbed with cold, too hampered by wet clothes and too disheartened to attempt any effective counter-attack. They scrambled for the farther bank, where they were picked off by bowmen and musketeers as they dragged themselves out of the river mud.

One sharp-witted freebooter, guessing the purpose of the boats, tossed his lantern into one of them. It burst mightily into flame; and the survivors of Kentigern's un-happy band were now exposed as if by daylight. Some men did manage to struggle up the muddy bank and into the darkness; but many were killed in the water, and a few drowned, lacking the strength to swim.

Kieron, as soon as he had grasped what was happening, had the wit to lower his head for a while below water and drift on with his boat. Luckily it was not the one that was fired. Downstream, and away from the glare of the flames, he managed to scramble to the bank.

Though he was numb with cold and almost exhausted, he forced himself to run through the darkness, falling down many times, but always managing to pick himself up, somehow. His limbs ached and his skin froze. Running, he knew, would be the only way he could keep himself alive. There were times when he wished to lie down and rest, even to sleep; but he would not allow himself to do so, realising that if he did, he might never rise.

He arrived back at the Misery in a pitiable condition just after daylight. He was not the first survivor to be lucky enough to make his way back. Several had preceded him. Several would come after.

He did not recognize Petrina. He did not seem to recognize anyone or anything. His eyes were vacant; and it was as if blind instinct had kept him going and had made him seek the security of his own folk.

Someone was holding him, someone was talking to him. He did not know who, nor did he understand the words. He must be among friends, he told himself vaguely, otherwise he would likely have been killed. But in case he had fallen into some kind of trap, he tried to raise the sword that he held, the sword that had not left his hand throughout that terrible journey down the river Arun.

He tried to raise the sword, and fell soundlessly. Petrina knelt by him, stroking him, weeping. She attempted to take the sword from his half-frozen fingers; but she could not.

He had a fever, and she nursed him for several days. At one time, the neddies thought him like to die. But he was young and strong; and Petrina warmed him with her body when the fever left him and he was held by a deathly chill. Presently, the chill faded and he became conscious and reasonable. He drank nourishing soup and felt a faint surge of strength in his limbs. He discovered, with some surprise, that he was destined to live.

One morning, he desired to wash himself and make himself presentable. Petrina brought him a mirror. He looked in it and was shocked to see the face of a stranger. A man with gaunt cheeks and deep lines on his face and forehead. A man with hair turning white.

It was a fine thing to have white hair when one was eighteen years old. How would he look when he was thirty? He shrugged. No matter. There was work to be done. Much, much work. What mattered was not how a man looked but what he had achieved.

Of the hundred men who set out on the ill-starred venture, but twenty-three returned, the rest being killed or taken. Kentigern was a broken man, his ability to make decisions seemingly paralysed by the magnitude of the disaster.

7

IN VARIOUS WAYS, the other seigneuries along the southern coast had fared quite as badly as the seigneurie of Arundel. Like the survivors of Arundel, the others had taken to the woods and to the downs, establishing temporary camps from which they made costly and at times disastrous counter-attacks upon the freebooters. The seigneuries had for so long been autonomous and self-sufficient that they had developed a fatal aversion to co-operating with each other and acting in unity. Their prejudices sprang from an almost racial fear of the evils of central government. For as far back as people could remember, seigneuries were united either by blood ties or by conquest; and it was a long time since any seigneur had been rash enough to attempt to subdue his neighbour by force of arms. Loose marital alliance had been both the strength and the weakness of the seigneurs. Now, confronted by invaders under a unified command, they were at a disadvantage.

It would be a considerable time, reasoned Kieron, before the people were able to abandon their traditional attitudes. A man from the next seigneurie was still regarded as a foreigner and treated with caution. How much more destruction would it take to make people realise that their only hope lay in working together? By the time people had come to their senses and the Grand Council had sent auxiliaries to aid them, Admiral Death would have an iron grip on the land he had conquered. And the people of Arundel, for whom he had the greatest concern, would remain fugitives, people of the woods, relapsing eventually into barbarism.

He had much time to reflect while he regained his strength and recovered from his illness. He began to take pleasure in Petrina once more, rejoicing in the sweet yielding of her body, giving her the seed of his loins and the love of his spirit. He did not need her to tell him when she had conceived. He knew. He had felt her body, relaxed yet taut, quivering joyfully beneath his. He had felt his seed leap joyfully into her womb, like salmon returning to the source of a known river.

One day he went to Kentigern. Now that he had hope of immortality, there was even more to fight for and to live for.

"I am going to build a hot-air balloon, Kentigern. A very large hot-air balloon. I am going to float it over the ships of Admiral Death and rain fire upon them from the sky. I need help. I need you to command men to help me."

Kentigern sat on a chair with a shawl round his shoulders, like Master Hobart. And, like Master Hobart, he coughed much and drank such strong spirits as were available to him.

"A hot-air balloon is heresy," he said thickly. "Holy Church will burn you, and possibly me also."

"We are all dying," said Kieron. "No man lives for ever. And what help has Holy Church given us in this time of disaster?"

Kentigern hiccuped. "The neddies have prayed for us."

"Has their prayer destroyed one of the freebooters?" demanded Kieron angrily.

"Who can say?"

"I can say. I would rather have one sword in my hand than the prayers of a hundred neddies behind me."

"You were right about the fire-boats ... Kieron, forgive me. My mind is not too clear. Construct the hot-air balloon, if you must. My judgment is fled."

"And I can have the men?"

"You shall have the men."

"And women to sew canvas and paper?"

"Those also."

"And you will allow me to choose my time and place?"

"I will allow you all these things," said Kentigern. "There is only one thing I will not allow you."

"What is that?"

"Failure. There has been too much failure. We cannot stand more. So, Kieron, my boy, understand that you stake your life upon this enterprise. If you fail I, poor thing that I am, will personally disembowel you for having persuaded me to damn my immortal soul for nothing."

"You ask much, Kentigern."

"I demand success, Kieron. That is all. When news of your enterprise goes forth — as it will — Holy Church will send to investigate. I hope I shall burn more tranquilly if the freebooters burn also." He gave a dreadful laugh. "I have seen much in my time. I have seen my master murdered and his women endure unspeakable things. Now we who live must entrust ourselves to a young man's madness."

Kieron gave a grim smile. "I would have more respect for Holy Church if it provided arms and men."

"The Church preaches peace and simplicity. In its wisdom it cares for our souls."

"Have you heard of anyone achieving peace at the stake, Kentigern?"

"Enough, boy! Destroy the freebooters, if you can, and I will gladly stand beside you when the reckoning comes."

"I shall need your words, on paper, sir. I shall need words and your signature, commanding men to assist me. Without such a paper, I cannot proceed."

"Then bring me ink, and I will commit my sin to writing . . . Do not fail, Kieron. That is all . . . They say you loved Mistress Alyx. Is that true?"

Kieron was too surprised to dissimulate. "It is true. We loved each other."

Again Kentigern laughed. "Forgive me. I laugh only at myself. I, too, loved her, do you see. But she was far above me. That is amusing, is it not? I would have given my life and honour to hold her, willingly, in my arms."

"I loved her and I held her," said Kieron evenly. "And it was sweet . . . That is all I care to say."

"It is enough. But why you, Kieron? Why the prentice painter?"

Kieron shrugged. "I do not know. Perhaps fortune favours him who dares."

8

IT WAS MANY days before Kieron was ready to begin construction of the hot-air balloon; but they were not days spent in idleness. First, he had to design the balloon and experiment with a model of it, and then he had also to assemble the materials for construction and train the people who would help him build it. Half the people at the Misery thought him mad, and the other half thought Kentigern mad. But, until a better authority were set over them, they would obey Kentigern; and he had put his name to a paper calling upon all able-bodied men and women to assist Kieron as needed.

Brothers Lemuel and Hildebrand were filled with horror. They remonstrated both with Kentigern and Kieron. Kentigern offered to countermand his orders if or when Holy Church mustered enough fighting men to push the freebooters into the sea. On being told that his immortal soul was endangered, he observed that he was presently more concerned with mortality than immortality. He even made so bold as to observe that the Divine Boy had accomplished little as yet to justify the devotion of the neddies and the obedience of the common people.

"Where was the protection of Ludd when my master was murdered and my mistress violated?" he demanded. "Nay, brothers, I understand your concern. But it cannot have escaped your notice that we live now in a disordered world. The days of peace and the seasons of prosperity are gone from us. Desperate men seek desperate remedies. Likely Kieron is mad and I am in my dotage; and you, good brothers, must do what you must. But plague me no more. If Kieron fails, he will die; and, doubtless, I also. But if he succeeds, let there be a reckoning."

"There will be a reckoning," promised Brother Lemuel. "Boyish pranks are one thing; but a deliberate attack upon doctrine is another. Make no mistake. Holy Church is patient. There will be a reckoning."

Kentigern gave him a twisted smile and took a deep draught of spirit. "I did not see you at the boats, brothers, when we drifted half-frozen down the Arun."

"It was not our place to be at the boats, Kentigern," retorted Brother Hildebrand. "We were at our devotions, praying for the success of your venture."

"Perhaps your prayers were not loud enough. Or perhaps the Divine Boy is deaf." Kentigern was quite pleased with himself. It was the first time he had ever blasphemed.

From Kieron, they got even shorter shrift.

"For the sake of a toy, Brother Sebastian wanted me to burn," he said grimly. "But Ludd, it seems, moves in mysterious ways. Sebastian is dead, while I live. An interesting thought . . . And now I am free to construct a sky machine for the benefit of our people." He lifted his sword, which he now carried with him always. "So I say to you, brothers, do not interfere with me or with those who help me, either by word or by deed. Else you may join Brother Sebastian in his perpetual slumber."

The brothers were horrified. No lay man had ever spoken to them like this before. Truly the world had changed.

"You threaten us?" said Brother Lemuel.

"I warn you, that is all. It is my first and final warning. Now leave me. I am busy."

The brothers retired in a state of shock. When they had recovered somewhat, they made plans. Brother Lemuel would go to London, to the office of the Inquisitor General. Brother Hildebrand would stay in the Misery and keep a record of all heretical acts. Then, when the Inquisitor General sent forces to re-establish the authority of the

Church, Brother Hildebrand would be able to bear witness against all those who had gone against the teachings of the Divine Boy.

There were no horses available — Kentigern saw to that — so Brother Lemuel would have to travel on foot. London was at least three day's march away. The brothers made no secret of their plans, and Kieron was fully informed of their intentions.

Petrina was horrified.

"Kieron, this time they will really burn you. Holy Church cannot ignore a direct challenge. Abandon the hot-air balloon, I beg you. Let us be patient. In time, the grand seigneurs will assemble forces sufficient to defeat the freebooters. Then we shall take up our ordinary lives once more."

Kieron held her close. "Rest easy, my love. You know, as I do, that with each day that passes, Admiral Death has a stronger hold upon our land. I will not wait for soldiers that may never come, or may come only to meet their doom. The only way to defeat the invader is in an element he cannot use. I will strike from the air. His soldiers do not have wings. He cannot elevate his cannon. I will strike from the air with fire. Holy Church will have little support if the ships of the freebooters are burning."

"In six days, Brother Lemuel could return with sufficient men to destroy you."

"Six days!" He laughed. "Brother Lemuel is not used to walking. He will have many blisters upon his feet. And will the Holy Office immediately despatch troops upon the word of a poor brother? No matter. In six days I shall be invulnerable."

"My love, I fear for you."

"Dear Petrina, I fear for us all."

9

HAVING OBTAINED AUTHORITY from Kentigern, Kieron was now confronted with the formidable task of translating a cherished dream into a practical reality. But a short time ago, he would have been saddened by the knowledge that the first use to which an aerial machine would be put would be as an instrument of destruction. If he had paused to reflect, he would have realised that the doctrine of the Luddite Church was not entirely spurious. Historically, the development of machines had amplified man's ability to destroy. The First and Second Men had destroyed their civilisation with their own ingenuity. From the standpoint of Holy Church there was no reason to suppose that men had now developed a greater wisdom that would sustain them in the creation of a third machine-based civilisation.

Kieron had no time to reflect upon such philosophical problems. Brother Lemuel was bound for London, and Admiral Death was consolidating his hold upon the southern coast. Kieron knew that he would have to produce a quick justification for his enterprise or pay the penalty of failure — either to Kentigern or Holy Church. It made little difference.

The first problem was one of design. In order to rain fire upon the ships of Admiral Death, Kieron would have to wait for a light offshore breeze, which would carry his hot-air balloon from its place of launching, over the free-booters' ships and then out to sea. Eventually, the hot-air balloon would come down in the ocean — it being un-likely that it could reach the coast of France, even if the wind held — and therefore whoever took to the skies with it would drown.

Unless the balloon carried something that could survive in the sea. A boat. A small boat. That would be the carriage in which the crew of the balloon would ride. It would have to be a very small boat and a very small crew. Otherwise, the size of the balloon would be huge beyond the ability of the people of Arundel to construct.

Kieron did much thinking, made sketches, made models. The balloon must not be in the shape of a sphere: it must be in the shape of a tapering sausage, corresponding roughly to the shape of the small boat that would be suspended from it.

Armed with Kentigern's authority, he sent men into Arundel to bring back all the linen, all the paper and needles and thread they could find. While they were gone, he spoke with Aylwin who, though pale and weak, was recovering from the loss of his hand.

"Aylwin, how do you fare?"

"I shall live," said Aylwin. "I shall live to be useless at my trade and a mockery to my fellows."

"How would you like to live for ever?"

"Kieron, I have no taste for jests."

"The bond between us still holds?"

"You know it does."

"To the death?"

"To the death . . . What do you require, Kieron?"

"I require you to journey with me suspended from a hot-air balloon. I require you to rain fire upon the freebooters."

"You would take a one-armed man on such a venture?" He thrust out the stump of his wrist, now mercifully hidden under clean bindings.

"I would take a friend," said Kieron. "I would take a man I trust. I would take one whose hatred of the freebooters passes beyond fear."

"Kieron, I am your man, as well you know. I am not brave, and this you also know. But I would dangle from the talons of an eagle if I could cause destruction to fall on those who have despoiled our peaceful seigneurie."

"We may not return from the venture."

Aylwin gave a faint smile. "I do not expect to. I have little reason for remaining alive ... Why, then, did you ask if I would like to live for ever?"

"Because our venture is one that men will remember. We shall begin anew the conquest of the skies and we shall strike terribly at those who have injured us."

"I require only one promise, Kieron. Give it, and I shall be happy."

"What is that?"

"I require to know that many shall die with us and because of us."

Kieron thought for a moment. "I cannot control the winds, Aylwin. And we must be sure, when all is ready, that the wind is our ally. But if we can take the hot-air balloon over the vessels at Little Hampton, I swear to you that men will perish in tens and hundreds. Is that enough?"

"It is enough." Aylwin laughed. "The dead freebooters in Arundel are your witnesses."

"So, then. Rest as much as you can. I have work to do. The time will be upon us sooner than you imagine."

10

KIERON PAID LITTLE attention to the passing of day and night. He worked by daylight. He worked by the light of whale-oil lamps and torches. He drew plans, made calculations, used models. He was distressed to find that the hot-air balloon would have to be far larger than he had anticipated. It would have to be fully fifteen metres long and two and a half metres in diameter; otherwise it would not carry the load he required. He instructed men in the construction of delicate frames from slender willow shoots. He showed women how they must sew linen and paper together to make a great envelope of the size he required. He set two prentice smiths to construct four braziers. He set woodmen to make charcoal, and others to make a small, light boat. He set boys to make ropes, and girls to fashion the ropes into a great net that would harness the hot-air balloon to the boat.

Kieron knew that the hot-air balloon must eventually come down to the sea, therefore its carriage must be in the form of a boat which could be quickly set loose upon the waves, so that the aeronauts would have some small hope of regaining land.

The Misery, which had been a refuge for despondent and beaten people, became transformed by Kieron's fanatical devotion to the hot-air balloon. Folk who would formerly have scoffed at the crazed notions of Kieron-head-in-the-air, became infected by his enthusiasm. Desperation was stronger than prejudice. They looked to him for hope. They looked to him and his fantastic project to inflict great losses upon the invaders. They recalled that already his fire-carts had inflicted more damage than all their fighting men combined. He had promised that, if they gave of their best to the construction of his aerial machine, he would rain fire upon the ships of Admiral Death. Kieron, though clearly mad, had already proved his talent for destruction. Therefore, they worked hard, not questioning his instructions or requirements. They would have followed a daemon if he had promised to burn the freebooters' ships.

Kieron slept little and ate little. He ate only when Petrina could find friends sufficiently courageous to drag him forcibly from his work, while she ladled out a helping of nourishing stew and swore that he would not be allowed to move until he had cleaned the platter. Sometimes, he would fling the platter away and shout obscenities. Sometimes, he would eat docilely, recalling that without food a man is weakened.

He no longer looked like a man of eighteen. His white hair had added years. The lines on his forehead and the hollowness of his cheeks had added character and power. He looked now like a man of thirty, a born leader. People became afraid of him, held him in awe. His sword rarely left his hand. He used it to measure linen and paper, to scratch diagrams in the ground. He used it to point, to threaten, to illustrate a command.

Kentigern was amazed at the changes that had taken place. Men and women who had formerly been listless went about their tasks with speed and energy. Because Kieron required of them as much as they were able to give. In return he promised vengeance.

There came a day when all the main constructions were finished. The envelope had been sewn, the net had been woven, the light boat had been built, the braziers had been worked. It was a day of caulking and seaming. The seams of the balloon and of the light boat were caulked by precious pitch taken from coal tar.

The pitch was hot and pungent. All those who came

close to the iron pots in which it simmered coughed with the fumes and dabbed at their streaming eyes.

Kentigern, himself coughing and cursing somewhat, came to look at the fabric of the great balloon, spread out on the grass while the pitch that sealed the joinings of fabric and paper lining cooled in the morning air.

"It is finished, Kieron?"

"It is finished."

"And it will fly?"

"If some fool does not tear the skin or set fire to it when we are heating the air, it will fly."

"You have worked hard."

Kieron shrugged. "Many have worked hard."

"You more than most. When did you last sleep?"

Kieron scratched his head and looked puzzled. "I forget. Does it matter? Yesterday, perhaps, or the day before."

Kentigern put a hand on his shoulder. "I confess, I did not believe you would achieve this much. Rest, now, boy. You are tired."

Kieron looked at him strangely. "Boy no more, Kentigern. Have I not done a man's work, here and elsewhere?"

"Ay, that you have. You are indeed a man, and I offered no offence."

Petrina had heard the exchange. "Make him rest, Kentigern. Command him to stop work. He kills himself."

Kentigern smiled. "Petrina, I command your man only to destroy freebooters. In all else, he commands himself."

Tears were running down Petrina's face. Kentigern supposed it was the smell of the pitch. But it was not the smell of the pitch. She wept when she looked at Kieron's white hair, at his dark eyes and hollow cheeks. She wept when she saw the sword that rarely left his hand. She wept when she saw the feverish brightness come upon him, a brightness and an energy not generated by good food and sound sleep. A daemonic power that compelled him to drive himself and others.

Suddenly, Kieron looked at her. He put his hands on her

shoulders and looked at her. It was the first time he seemed to have seen her, or even been aware of her, in days.

"Fret not, my love. Presently, all shall be as you wish ... Do you remember when we were children? We came here to the Misery one hot afternoon in late summer, and we lay under the great beech tree, and I told you I wanted to fly."

The anxiety on Petrina's face softened. "I remember. Plums and apples. I ate too many and had much pain."

Kieron laughed. "Plums and apples and the bright world of childhood."

Kentigern coughed noisily. "I am an intruder. I will go. When will you test the balloon, Kieron?"

Kieron did not look at him. "This afternoon, when I have eaten and held converse with my wife. This afternoon, Kentigern, you shall see history made."

Kentigern retired, coughing and muttering to himself.

"Plums and apples," said Kieron. "We both ate too many ... Do you remember what else we talked about?"

Petrina smiled. "I told you that my mother had consulted the astrologer Marcus. He said that you would be a grand master of your art and that I should bear three children." She sighed. "So much for the hopes and visions of childhood. We live now in a world where these things cannot come to pass."

"Do we?" asked Kieron excitedly. "Do we indeed? What else did Marcus say? Can you remember?"

Petrina's forehead crinkled. "He said ... He said that your greatest painting would be of a terrible fish that destroys folk by burning them. I can recollect no more."

"Then let us redeem the astrologer's reputation," said Kieron. He turned from her and snatched a large brush that had been used for daubing hot pitch upon the seams of the balloon. He dipped it into one of the iron pots and then approached the laid out fabric.

Skilfully and quickly, he painted a great staring eye at the head of the balloon. Then he dipped the brush again and painted below the eye a huge cavernous mouth, with rows of sharp teeth. His strokes were swift and sure. At the far end of the balloon, he painted a great black tail.

"Here is my greatest painting, Petrina. The shark that swims through the air and devours men . . . Now let us go and eat, then let us lie together. For this afternoon the great fish of death takes to the sky."

II

KIERON SAW TO the braziers, made sure that the charcoal was glowing but not spitting out sparks or flames. Then he made sure that the men and women who were to hold the balloon while it filled with hot air knew exactly what to do. Then he tested the net that harnessed the balloon to the boat it would raise. Finally, he gave the signal for the orifices in its underbelly to be held over the braziers so that hot air would enter inside the fabric.

The flat envelope began to swell. Presently, it lifted from the grass. Presently it hung suspended over the boat, with the braziers forcing in more and yet more hot air.

Kieron and Aylwin climbed into the boat.

"Well, Aylwin?"

"Well, Kieron?"

"Shortly we shall be airborne. If you have no stomach for the venture, now is the time to speak."

"I have already spoken. So have you."

"Enough, then. Let us see how the fish of death takes to the sky." He signalled to the men holding ropes attached to the bow and the stern of the small boat.

They paid out. Slowly the balloon began to rise.

"More heat to number one brazier," called Kieron. "We are not on an even keel."

Aylwin took the bellows and, resting them on the arm that lacked a hand, pumped away at number one. The charcoals glowed brightly and the heat balance was maintained.

The small boat, in which Kieron crouched at one end and Aylwin at the other with the metal tray supporting the four braziers swaying a little between them, had risen above the heads of the people below. Kieron signalled for more rope to be paid out, then used hand bellows to make the charcoal glow more brightly in the two braziers he tended. Aylwin also used his bellows. Kieron felt the extra lift.

"Airborne!" he exclaimed triumphantly. "Airborne at last!" It was as if the clumsy balloon swelled with life, straining impatiently at the ropes that held the small boat, at stem and stern, suspended from it.

There was a great cheer from below. Aylwin looked over the side and stared down at the group of upturned faces. Kieron signalled for more rope to be paid out. Slowly, majestically the balloon rose above the tree-tops of the Misery. It was as if, now that it was truly in the element for which it was designed, the balloon had mysteriously gained physical grace.

Kieron signalled for yet more rope to be loosed. The balloon was now more than fifty metres above the Misery, swaying and riding upon air currents like a boat on a mild sea swell.

Aylwin, white-faced, looked anxiously at Kieron. "Are we not high enough, Kieron? Truly it is awesome."

The wind seemed to swallow his words. Ropes and timbers creaked, the charcoal in the braziers glowed golden.

"Look south," called Kieron. "Look south. There lies the enemy."

The air was clear, and the Misery was no more than nine or ten kilometres from the sea. Aylwin followed Kieron's gaze. He could see the ocean. He could see the far horizon. He could see sunlight upon water. And, at Little Hampton, he could see the masts of ships, huddled together like toy boats on a great pond. He laughed nervously. "They do not look so fearsome from this distance, Kieron."

"Nor will they seem fearsome when we pass over them and drop fire bombs upon their decks. We shall cause such destruction, Aylwin, that men will speak of it in wonder in the years to come."

Aylwin shuddered. "How can you be so sure? How can you be so sure that we shall succeed, that we shall aim well, that the fires will not be put out, that the balloon will not be destroyed, that we shall even pass close enough to the ships?"

Kieron gave a terrible smile. "Of late, I have given much thought to the problem of how to inflict death and destruction. It is a new trade I have learned, and one for which, as you know, I have some talent. The secret of this trade of dealing in death is to pay great attention to detail. While I have been building this shark of the sky, this formidable monster filled only with hot air, I have also given thought to our means of delivering fire. Rest easy, Aylwin. If we die — and we may — we shall give an excellent accounting."

He was aware of voices, shouts from below. He looked down at the people in the Misery and saw that two of the men who held the ropes attached to the small boat had been pulled clear of the ground. They hung on to their ropes perilously, shouting, imploring.

Again Kieron smiled. "We have excellent lift, I see. More than I had hoped for. Therefore we shall carry more weight than I had hoped. But now let us return to earth. Quench number one brazier, Aylwin, and I will quench number four. Thus shall we return gently to our friends."

Aylwin and Kieron took small flasks of water and poured them very slowly over the glowing charcoals. There was much sizzling, and hot steam rose, giving the balloon more temporary lift. The men hanging on the ropes cried out with alarm.

But as the heat faded, the shark of the sky began to lose height. Smoothly and slowly it sank down to earth. Kieron gave a great sigh of regret as he found himself below the tree-tops of the Misery once more. Presently, there was a slight jolt as the boat grounded.

Kentigern was the first to greet him. "Well, Kieron, are you satisfied?"

"I am satisfied."

"And you still believe that you can carry fire to the freebooters' ships?"

"I know that I can. More even than I had calculated."

Kentigern gave a sigh of relief. "Well, then, we shall not be damned in vain. While you have been labouring upon the construction of this monstrous thing, others have been engaged in more civilised pursuits. Beer has been brewed. Come, let us drink to the success of the venture."

"You drink," said Kieron. "I have work to do."

"What work? The balloon is finished."

"I wish to experiment with the best means of delivering fire. When you have drunk your toasts, Kentigern, send men to seek barrels of whale oil, flasks, goat-skin bottles, bales of straw, lard, pitch — anything that will burn fiercely."

"You are a dedicated man, Kieron."

Kieron laughed dreadfully. "Yes. I am dedicated to destruction."

12

TWO DAYS LATER, the wind blew gently but steadily from the north. The sky was clear, blue as a heron's egg, and the downs were bathed in a quiet autumnal beauty.

A strange caravan left the Misery. Preceded by a column of foot soldiers headed by Liam, Kentigern and Isidor rode side by side on horseback, the two horses harnessed together by a reversed yoke passing under their bellies. In the centre of the yoke was a stout iron ring. Through it passed a rope. The rope rose taughtly upwards to be hooked on the stem and stern of the boat that hung from Kieron's hot-air balloon ten metres above.

Kieron had painted a name on the slender craft. The name was: *Mistress Fitzalan's Revenge*. Petrina wept when she saw it. But she took care not to let Kieron see her weeping.

They had made their goodbyes but an hour before — while Aylwin was confessing his sins to Brother Hildebrand, who, though he had faithfully recorded all heretical acts, saw no reason why he should not give absolution to a mutilated boy who was going to almost certain death.

"I will love you always," Petrina had said, dry-eyed at the last so that her man should not be weakened.

"And I will love you always."

"More than you loved Alyx Fitzalan?" As soon as the words were out, Petrina could have cut off her tongue. This was no time for barbs. Kieron was about to put himself in peril of his life.

He was not angry. He held her close; and, in the sight

of many men and women, placed his hand upon her breast.

"More fully than I ever loved Alyx." He smiled, glancing at the balloon that was already filled with hot air and swayed as if impatient at its mooring. "I have already accommodated the astrologer Marcus by painting a fish that will destroy men by fire. There will be time, will there not, for you to do your part and bear three children?"

She kissed him. "Please Ludd, there will be time. Come back, Kieron. That is all."

Then he and Aylwin had seated themselves in *Mistress Fitzalan's Revenge* and had checked all the strange equipment that littered the craft and even hung suspended from hooks over its side. After satisfying himself that supplies of charcoal, flasks of water, goatskins of whale oil, ropes and grapnels and the small tightly packed bales of straw that had soaked overnight in oil were all in position, Kieron applied more fuel to the braziers and used the bellows. *Mistress Fitzalan's Revenge* lifted slowly from her mooring, and was manhandled into position above the two restive horses. The rope was passed through the ring on the yoke and made fast; and the fantastic caravan moved off, the horses snorting and whinnying nervously as they sustained a load, an upward pull, that was against nature.

Kieron's plan was that Kentigern and Isidor should draw the hot-air balloon as near as possible to the windward side of the vessels at Little Hampton. When he judged that he was in position where the offshore wind would carry him over the freebooters' ships, he would release the rope that held *Mistress Fitzalan's Revenge* to the yoke between the horses. After that, all depended upon luck, skill, destiny. Kentigern, Isidor and the foot soldiers would stay to observe, if they were not attacked. If they were to be attacked, they would endeavour to retreat to Arundel and observe matters with a spy-glass.

The strange cavalcade passed through the town of Arundel without hindrance, disturbing only the rats and sea birds attending to the rotting corpses of freebooters who had perished in the path of the fire-carts.

As *Mistress Fitzalan's Revenge* passed the castle, Kieron and Aylwin found that they were high enough to look over the walls. The funeral pyre was now no more than a great heap of ash, disturbed occasionally by gusts of wind.

"Rest easy, my love," said Kieron softly. "This day there will be a reckoning."

Unmolested, the column marched down the hill, across the bridge over the river Arun and took the road to the sea.

It was a beautiful day; a day for strolling among the downs and marvelling at the secrets of nature. It was a day for riding, or for painting, or for grinding corn, or for beating a ploughshare in a forge. It was a day for creation, not for destruction. And yet . . . And yet there were times when it was necessary to destroy before one could create . . .

"How do you feel, Aylwin? Are you warm enough?" Kieron had made him put on a sheepskin coat, realising that it would be cold work when they rose a hundred or more metres into the sky.

"I am warm, Kieron. And you?"

"I also. This day we shall strike a great blow."

Aylwin shivered. "It is that thought which makes my heart cold, though my flesh be warm. Shall we succeed?"

"You have my word. If Kentigern and Isidor can get us to true windward, you have my word."

"And if they can not?"

"We shall strike another day."

But things went well. Things went well until they came within two kilometres of Little Hampton. It was there that they encountered the first of Admiral Death's outposts. It was not greatly manned — a dozen men, no more.

The foot soldiers advanced and attacked the outpost. Bows and crossbows against muskets and crossbows.

Seventeen men of Arundel fell in destroying twelve of the freebooters. And they could not destroy them before a fire signal was sent.

Kieron called down to Kentigern. "We have not much time. Leave the road and strike west. We must be to true windward."

"We must attend to our wounded," called Kentigern.

"No time. Leave the road. Leave a few men if you must, but ride west."

"Damn you, Kieron. You do not have a bolt in your body. Can you hear their cries?"

"I can. Ride west. Waste no time."

"I will not."

"Then you are a fool," said Kieron. "If you do not ride west, I will rain the fire on you that I hoped to rain upon the freebooters." He lighted a torch from a brazier and held it close to one of the oil-soaked bales that hung from the side of *Mistress Fitzalan's Revenge*. "Do you hear me?"

"I hear you. Damn you for ever, there will be a reckoning."

"There will indeed," said Kieron tranquilly. "Ride west."

Kentigern shouted a command. The remainder of the foot soldiers — no more than seven or eight — stayed with their fallen comrades. Kentigern and Isidor turned their horses and cantered across a field of burnt stubble. There was a high hedge at the end of it.

"Leap it!" called Kieron. "The balloon will give you lift!" He signalled to Aylwin to pump bellows at number one while he pumped bellows at number four. The charcoals glowed, the balloon strained. The horses that Isidor and Kentigern rode took a leap of nearly two metres height almost simultaneously. Both landed fair.

Aylwin and Kieron had braced themselves. The balloon, and the boat suspended under it, had begun to sway rhythmically as Kentigern and Isidor took to the fields;

but the movement was not jerky, the ropes tightening and then slacking somewhat to accommodate the motion of the horses. Even when they took the two-metre leap, the only sensation experienced by the aeronauts was one of smooth rise and smooth fall.

Kieron kept his eyes on the vessels at Little Hampton, now plainly in view but still about two kilometres away, since Kentigern and Isidor were riding parallel with the coast. He saw also that a group of horsemen were already coming at speed towards the outpost that had been destroyed.

"Hurry," he called down. "The freebooters send horsemen. Hurry and take us to true windward."

Kentigern, red-faced and angry, looked up. "How much farther, madman?"

"Stop about the middle of the next field. I will test the wind."

The next hedge was not so high. The horses took it easily.

It must be, thought Kieron with elation, the strangest sight ever seen in Britain: two horsemen drawing a hot-air balloon above and behind them like a monstrous kite. Two horsemen drawing a hot-air balloon from which was suspended a boat containing two young men and their weaponry — all that the seigneurie of Arundel could put against the might of Admiral Death.

He laughed aloud.

Aylwin regarded him anxiously. "What is it, Kieron? If there is something at which I may laugh, tell me. I would greatly value the ability to laugh now."

"Look at those ships."

"I have looked. They are formidable."

"Now look at us."

Aylwin looked. At the balloon, at Kieron, at the boat and its contents, at the horsemen below. Miraculously, he, too, began to laugh.

"Kieron, my friend, you were insane for conceiving this

venture, and I for consenting to it. You are right to laugh. We are absurd."

"Not absurd, sublime."

Aylwin sighed. "It is a great day for dying."

"No, my friend, not for us. It is a great day for destroying."

"I read death."

"I read destruction."

"Well, babblers," called Kentigern, bringing the horses to a halt. "Are we to windward?"

Kieron let a fragment of paper fall from the boat. It drifted towards Little Hampton as it fell. It drifted towards the cluster of vessels, but not to dead centre.

"To the edge of the field, Kentigern."

Kentigern swore and spurred his horse. Isidor kept perfect pace with him.

Again Kieron let a fragment of paper fall. It drifted true before it reached the ground. Only let the wind hold, he prayed. Only let it hold steady for a half-hour, no more.

He called down to Kentigern: "We have arrived at the spot, Kentigern. Thank you. Thank you for giving me this day."

Kentigern looked up, shielding his eyes against the sun. "You are a fool, Kieron, but a brave one. I know not if you are touched with greatness or with madness. Farewell."

"See to Petrina, if —"

Kentigern held up a hand. "Fear not, boy." Then he said with a strange formality: "She shall be as my daughter, and I will spill blood in her defence. This I swear."

"Then I am in your debt for ever." Kieron signalled to Aylwin. Together they unhooked the rope. The balloon rose.

Isidor put his hands to his mouth. "Good hunting, shark of the sky. Eat many freebooters this day."

The balloon rose, stretching and straining almost like a living thing. For the last time, Kieron looked at the horsemen below and waved. They seemed tiny men sitting upon tiny animals. They seemed like strange insects, earth-bound.

Then he gave his attention to the vessels at Little Hampton. The vessels towards which *Mistress Fitzalan's Revenge* slowly drifted, in an eerie, windwashed silence.

13

FOR A MOMENT or two, it seemed as if the entire world was a frozen tableau, the only movement being that of the hot-air balloon as it continued to drift and rise slowly. Toy ships lay ahead, toy horsemen were held to the earth below. Kieron experienced a great surge of confidence and power, rejoicing in the silence, the smooth and beautiful movement, rejoicing that he was now free in the element for which he had been born.

Aylwin broke the spell. "More charcoals, Kieron?" he called anxiously.

Kieron's mind returned to matters practical. The balloon, he calculated, was already at topsail height and still rising, the drift was slow — no more than a fast walking pace. If the breeze did not stiffen, the balloon would reach Admiral Death's flotilla in ten or fifteen minutes.

"No, Aylwin. The heat balance is good. Let us put our main set of grapnel ropes overboard. Pay out about twenty metres of rope and make fast. Then check that your fire-bales are ready for casting off."

Four grapnels, two from the stem and two from the stern, were lowered. The ropes swayed in the breeze. The iron claws of the grapnels glinted in the sunlight. Kieron hoped to engage the grapnels in the rigging of the ships, using them as a temporary anchor.

"My fire-bales are ready, Kieron."

"Mine also. Is your torch to hand?"

"It lies at my feet . . . Are you afraid?"

"Yes, I am afraid. But I am also happy. No, happy is not the right word. Eager — perhaps that is the word."

"I am greatly afraid. You should have chosen a braver man."

Kieron smiled. "I chose well . . . They cut off your hand, Aylwin. They did unspeakable things to those we love. Remember that."

"You give me strength."

"You have your own strength. This day we two shall give a great accounting. Does that make you feel better?"

"It makes me feel like a god."

Kieron laughed. "Truly, then, we are as gods. Only men strike from the land or the sea. We strike from the air."

The balloon drifted inexorably closer to the vessels at Little Hampton. Kieron saw much activity upon their decks. Puffs of smoke appeared at their gun ports; but the guns could not be elevated high enough for their cannon balls to come near the balloon.

"See," said Kieron, "they panic, they waste black powder."

"Soon we shall be in musket range."

"Then let us have more height. Let us see their musketeers shoot into the sun."

More charcoals were fed into the braziers. Kieron and Aylwin used their bellows. The balloon climbed.

Now the cluster of vessels was no more than a hundred metres away. Again, Kieron estimated the rate of rise, the the rate of drift.

"Lower the grapnel ropes another fifteen metres."

"Ay, ay."

"Make ready to engage."

"Kieron?"

"Yes, Aylwin?"

"Ludd bless you for giving me this chance."

"Say no more. Act only on my command. We are about to burn vermin."

Two of the grapnels caught in the rigging of a vessel lying close between two others. But the pull of the wind took *Mistress Fitzalan's Revenge* away from the vertical, so that directly beneath Kieron there was nothing but water.

"Haul in the grapnel ropes," he shouted. "We must be above the deck."

Aylwin tried to haul in. So did Kieron. But the lift was too strong.

"Quench a fourth part of number one brazier, and I will quench a fourth part of number four."

They took flasks of water and poured sparingly round the charcoals. Again, there was the temporary lift as the hot steam rose. But after a few seconds they were able to haul in the grapnel ropes. Meanwhile, freebooters had begun to climb the rigging, and musketeers on deck were shooting at the shark of the sky.

Kieron looked down and saw the men climbing the rigging to free the grapnels and the men on deck shooting with their muskets. He did not care. *Mistress Fitzalan's Revenge* was now directly above the vessel she had attacked.

"Two fire-bales!" shouted Kieron hoarsely. "Two from me also."

He and Aylwin lighted their torches from the braziers and put fire to two oil-soaked bales as they released them from their hooks.

In a great shower of sparks and flames and oil, the bales fell down to the deck, one of Aylwin's fiery missiles carrying two freebooters from the rigging with it. Their screams died with two dull thuds as they hit the deck, one of them falling directly into the flames.

The binding of the bales broke upon impact and the burning remnants scattered upon the deck. The smoke billowed high, and the freebooters drew back in panic; but there were those also who had already begun to organise a bucket chain to quench the flames. Kieron sent two goat-skins of whale oil after the bales. His aim was good. One of the goatskins burst on top of an already substantial blaze, rivulets of fire running across the wooden deck. Two or three of the freebooters, caught by the fierce heat, jumped overboard. The other goatskin exploded upon an open hatchway, leading a trail of fire deep into the ship.

There was pandemonium below. No longer did any of the freebooters attempt to bring down the shark of the sky with musket fire. They were too busy trying to extinguish the raging flames, or trying to save themselves. More and more men jumped overboard.

Kieron, looking down, was satisfied that the vessel was doomed. Now was the time to see to the safety of *Mistress Fitzalan's Revenge*. The heat was so intense that burning fragments of straw were whirled aloft in a fierce updraught. It would be absurd if the hot-air balloon were destroyed by its own weapons.

"Release the grapnel ropes!" he shouted to Aylwin. "When we are free, lower the next set. The wind will give us one more vessel."

The grapnel ropes were released, and the hot-air balloon rose suddenly. The lightening of the load in *Mistress Fitzalan's Revenge* had given it great buoyancy. It soared up from the stricken vessel, like a bird set free. It was necessary for Kieron and Aylwin to completely extinguish two braziers to bring the balloon down to the level of the next vessel's rigging.

They had only two grapnel ropes left. The next vessel was a hundred metres away, direct to windward. It was the largest vessel in the flotilla. It carried a flag on which was the gilded emblem of a death's head. Kieron felt a brief surge of pleasure. This second vessel, the only other ship he could hope to attack, was the flag ship. He prayed that Admiral Death would be aboard.

The hot-air balloon drifted towards it, amid a hail of musket fire. Musket balls penetrated *Mistress Fitzalan's Revenge* and the still taut fabric of the shark of the sky. But neither Aylwin nor Kieron was hit. The two grapnel ropes swayed ominously in the breeze. One of the grapnels caught in the rigging. *Mistress Fitzalan's Revenge* swung crazily.

The crew of the flag ship had learned much from what had happened to the other vessel. Many armed men were already in the rigging. Some paused in their ascent to fire hand guns, but with little hope of hitting the two attackers swinging in their frail craft thirty metres higher than any freebooters could climb; while others, more intelligently, sought to reach the grapnel and cut it loose before any more could be attached.

Kieron saw that there was little time left. "The bales! Drop all the bales." He shouted. "Aim for the highest men."

Aylwin saw the danger, and understood. He and Kieron put torch to the remaining six bales and sent them hurtling down. Aylwin's aim was good. He seemed to have the knack of it. His first bale slithered and bounced down the rigging, leaving burning straw and burning rope in its path, causing two men to jump into the sea to avoid it. His second bale carried away a man who had almost reached the grapnel rope. Man and bale fell to the deck together in a starburst of death and fire. Kieron's first two bales were less successful, one missing the vessel completely as *Mistress Fitzalan's Revenge* swung in the wind. The other falling clear to the deck, but where it fell there was no fire to be seen, the flames, perhaps, having been extinguished in the manner of its descent.

Aylwin sent down his third bale and was gratified to see it enlarge the fire caused by his first. He laughed aloud with pleasure. As with the first vessel attacked, some weak hearts were already beginning to abandon ship.

Kieron also sent down his third bale. It fell truly, but he was mystified to see no burst of fire as it hit the deck. Perhaps the clouds of smoke obscured it, or perhaps it had passed clean into the depths of the ship through an open hold or hatchway.

Aylwin was fairly jumping with excitement. Kieron saw that the rigging was now burning and that soon the grapnel that held them to the vessel would be burnt loose.

"The goatskins!" he called. "Drop the goatskins of oil!"

There were not many left. Kieron began to drop his supply over the side as fast as he could reach them, not pausing to see where they fell.

The deck of the vessel was now a blazing inferno. Aylwin either had not heard Kieron's command about the goatskins, or he did not care. He stood up in the small craft — a perilous thing to do — and hung on to one of the ropes that held it to the net harness over the shark of of the sky.

"Sit down!" Kieron called.

Aylwin did not respond. His face was alive with immense pleasure. He waved the stump of his wrist proudly and shouted words that Kieron could not comprehend down at the freebooters.

Suddenly Kieron felt a sharp lift as the grapnel came free from the burning rigging. The balloon soared. At almost the same instant, there was a great explosion below as the ship blew itself apart. Evidently, fire had reached a supply of black powder.

The balloon's own buoyancy, relieved as it was of the weight of the bales and the goatskins of whale oil, together with the force of the explosion, shot it upwards like a cork from a shaken bottle of sparkling wine.

Aylwin uttered a great cry, and seemed to leap from the craft into the air. Kieron caught a brief glimpse of him, apparently motionless, spreadeagled in the sky, a look of great contentment on his face. Then Alywin fell; and Kieron lost his balance as *Mistress Fitzalan's Revenge* rose. And the miller's apprentice was seen no more.

Somehow, as he sprawled in the bottom of his frail craft and hung on for dear life, Kieron managed to keep his wits about him. He looked up and saw that the force of the explosion had blown various small holes in the fabric of the balloon. But, as yet, the rents were small.

Presently, the balloon became steady. Kieron picked himself up and glanced cautiously over the side of his small boat. The sight took his breath away. He had never been so awed, so exhilarated. He must be at least five hundred metres above the ocean.

There below, like tiny toy boats at the edge of a great mill-pond, lay the freebooters' ships. He counted eleven all together — and four were burning! The explosion must have spread the fire to the two nearest ships. The pall of smoke was heavy; but it was clear that three of the burning vessels were certainly beyond saving.

From the height he had attained, everything that was happening below seemed to be in slow motion. Regardless of his own safety and the trim of the balloon, he studied the effects of his attack carefully. It would be something to remember always — no matter how long or how short a time he had left to live.

After a few moments he noticed that the most devastated ship, almost a burning hulk and probably the one that had suffered the explosion, was moving, drifting with the current. Evidently it had been torn free from its moorings by the blast. And now, no doubt assisted by the current of the river Arun in its sea reach, the vessel was bearing down upon two of its fellows, as yet undamaged.

Even from this great height — the balloon was still rising — Kieron could see the flurry of activity on the decks and in the rigging of the threatened ships as seamen desperately weighed anchor and made sail in their attempts to escape a fiery doom.

As Kieron watched, his heart swelling with pride at the destruction that had been wrought, there was a huge puff of smoke from one of the other burning ships. Spars and fragments of timber flew out from it. The sound of the explosion came afterwards, dulled by distance, but still sounding as sweet music.

For a moment, Kieron forgot his plight. "See, Aylwin!" he called. "Have I not more than kept my promise?" But even as he spoke, he realised that there was no Aylwin to witness. "No matter, my friend, my brother. I saw the look upon your face, and you were content. Rest easy. It has been a great accounting. Likely, I will join you soon."

One of the vessels in the path of the fiery hulk could not get under way fast enough. In its death frenzy the burning ship struck the other vessel amidships. "See, Aylwin," said Kieron stupidly, knowing full well that Aylwin was not there to hear, but still feeling an overwhelming need to speak. "The destruction multiplies. Of eleven ships, we have now accounted for five. We two poor prentices have accomplished more than could be achieved by a thousand armed men on land. Did I not offer you the chance to live for ever?"

And then the tears came. Alone in the sky, Kieron was not ashamed to weep as a child. It was a private luxury. No one would ever know. Presently, no doubt, he would drown — he knew nothing of the skill of handling a small boat far out to sea — but it was a good day on which to die, as Aylwin had already discovered.

"Kristen, my mother," he sobbed, "Gerard, my father. I am sorry that I could not become a great painter as you required ... Master Hobart, you who gave me great love, sorrow not that I forsook the brush and pigments. *Mistress Fitzalan's Leap* was truly your painting. I was but an extended hand, a youthful eye ... Alyx, my dear one, I would have defended you, if I could. But you, whom I loved and who are now dead, if there be an after life, which I being perhaps purblind, doubt, look upon what I have done ... Petrina, my wife, my seed has entered your womb, and I pray that a child may be born. I hope you will remember this day with pride."

Kieron was exhausted both in the body and in the spirit. Days and nights of hard work and hard thought, the elation he had felt while fire was being rained upon the freebooters, the sadness of Aylwin's death — all these things had drained him of emotion. He was too tired to think clearly, too tired to act. He lay back in *Mistress Fitzalan's Revenge* and closed his eyes. At the best, he thought drowsily, life was but a short journey from darkness to darkness. He had been lucky, very lucky, to know the love of fair women, to paint a great portrait, to construct a hot-air balloon and sail the skies like a god, bringing death to those who trafficked in death. Yes, he had been very lucky for a poor young man barely turned eighteen. A look of great peace came over his face as he slept.

14

TWO BRAZIERS STILL burned; and the shark of the sky, lightened of the greater part of its burden, continued to rise. Kieron, still profoundly asleep or unconscious, was not aware that the balloon had climbed to nearly two thousand metres above the level of the sea. It passed through a tenuous cloud layer; and dew formed upon his face and hands and hair. Then it rose once more into the gold of sunlight.

The dew made Kieron shiver, and he awoke. He awoke to find himself above gold-capped clouds, drifting in realms of infinite beauty. He looked down at the islands of cloud. They seemed substantial enough to step upon.

He marvelled at the splendour of the sight. "Perhaps no man has seen this from an aerial machine for centuries," he said aloud. "Likely I am the first of the Third Men to look down upon such clouds and behold their glory. Truly, I am fulfilled."

But the charcoals in the braziers were burning low and the rents in the balloon were releasing hot air. Kieron was granted only a minute or two of ecstasy before the balloon began to fall through the cloud layer.

He watched, fascinated, as the white mist closed about him and the moisture of the clouds caused the dying charcoals to sizzle and spit. The balloon descended slowly, as if it were reluctant to end this its final flight. The fabric, now slack, was flapping noisily, and the holes in it grew larger. Kieron gazed gloomily down at the sea. There was a light swell; but it was not enough, he thought, to swamp the boat. He looked all round for land, but could see none. Perhaps Aylwin had had the better end after all — a quick clean death. Kieron was no seaman and, despite the quietness of the water, held his prospects to be poor.

Mistress Fitzalan's Revenge hit the water quite hard. For a moment or two, the fabric of the balloon was billowing all about him as if it intended to claim yet one more victim in its death throes. He felt hot charcoals against his legs and tried to cry out with the pain; hot linen and scorched paper pressed about his face as if to smother him.

But presently, relieved of its burden, the tattered shark of the sky tried to rise once more. Hastily, Kieron unhooked the harness ropes. Flapping noisily and self-destructively, the balloon lifted itself like a doomed beast, hovered uncertainly, then rolled over on its side and fell to the sea. Before it sank beneath the water Kieron saw once again the baleful eyes and toothy open mouth he had painted. He smiled, remembering once more the astrologer's prediction, remembering that day long ago when all the world, it seemed, was young.

And now he was alone on a wide sea; and he had no strength and no food, and little hope. It was odd that he should have neglected to stock the vessel with food, particularly so since he had not forgotten a pair of light oars. A man could not row far on an empty belly. Perhaps he had known all along that he did not intend to row far.

He felt even more weary now that all was over. I will rest, he thought. I will close my eyes and rest and think on all that has happened, and try to make my peace. Sooner or later, the sea will receive me. And that will be the end of Kieron-head-in-the-air.

He lay down in the boat, making himself as comfortable as possible, drawing his clothes about him. The motion of the boat was gentle and soothing. It reminded him of a long-lost summer when his father had made a small hammock for him and had hung it between two apple-trees. Kieron had lain on the hammock with his eyes closed, making it sway gently, and pretending that he was a mysterious and magical lord of the air.

"Well, for a short time I became a lord of the air," he murmured. "That much, at least, was achieved."

15

"*Comment vous appelez-vous?*" Kieron felt a sword point at his chest. He tried to reach for his own sword, which had lain all the while by his side in the small boat. He could not find it. The sword at his chest pricked him, and he lay still, trying to gather his wits.

"*Je m'appelle Kieron. Je suis Anglais.*" His small knowledge of French had been gained from the occasional matelot who had ventured inland to Arundel. He realised that it would not stretch far.

"*Alors ... Vous connaissez l'Amiral Mort?*"

"*Oui. Je le connais.*"

"*Vous êtes ami ou ennemi?*"

Now there was a life or death question! Kieron did not care greatly which way it went.

"*Je suis l'ennemi d'Amiral Mort. Parlez-vouz Anglais?*"

There was a laugh in the semi-darkness. Kieron looked away from the swaying lantern that dazzled him and saw that the sky, dominated by a bright full moon, was rich with stars. The lantern waved high above his head, but he looked past it and concentrated on the beauty of the night sky. If he were to be killed, the stroke would not be long in coming.

"*Un petit peu,*" said the stranger. "I speak the little English ... You can stand?"

"I think so."

"*Bon.* You will please to follow aboard my ship. You see the rope ladder?"

"Yes."

"You can climb it? "

"Yes. What about my sword?"

"Rest easy. I have it. Come now. Your boat is made fast."

Kieron climbed up on to the deck of what looked like a small fishing vessel. The lantern had been held almost directly above him by one of the crew. Now that he was no longer dazzled by it, and now that he had fully regained his senses, he was able to see quite clearly in the moonlight. Yes, perhaps a fishing vessel — or one of Admiral Death's supply tenders. It was odd that the Frenchman had immediately mentioned Admiral Death . . .

"You are fishermen?"

"*Comment?*"

"Fishermen. You take fish from the sea?"

"*Ah, pêcheurs!*" Again there was a laugh. "Yes, Monsieur Kieron, you shall say we are fishermen. It is a joke. It is good."

Kieron glanced round him. It really was a very small vessel, carrying, perhaps, a crew of four or five at most. One man was at the wheel, one man had held the lantern, and there was the stranger who now confronted him. He spoke with authority and carried himself with authority. Very likely, he was the master.

Kieron gazed at him in the moonlight. He was heavily bearded, but he seemed like a young man. He spoke like a young man also.

Kieron wished he had his sword in his hand. But it was in the hand of the French captain. The thought was irritating.

"If you are going to kill me, strike now. I will not play games. The day has been good, and I am content."

"Monsieur Kieron! Who speaks of killing? We find you — *heureusement*, luckily, because Etienne sees well in the dark — we find you, I say, drifting in a small boat. You were already bound for death, *monsieur*."

That was something Kieron could not answer.

"It is we who must make the questions, *monsieur*. For

what we know, you may be — how I say it? — *un homme dangereux, un félon, un pirate, peut-être.*"

"*Monsieur*, I do not understand," said Kieron wearily. "My name is Kieron Joinerson and I am a man of the seigneurie of Arundel on the island of Britain. You find me adrift in a small boat because I have this day inflicted much damage on the vessels of Admiral Death. I struck at him from the air, having constructed a hot-air balloon. It is something he will remember. Now, do with me what you will."

"*Un ballon!*" exclaimed the Frenchman excitedly. "*Vous êtes l'homme du ballon? Magnifique! Monsieur*, forgive me. I am *Jean-Baptiste Girod, capitaine* of the *Marie-France* of *Arromanches*. Today I am make — make is right? — the reconnaissance of the forces of Admiral Death. We in France know that this is bad man, very bad man. We know he hold some British coast. We wish to understand his plan. Today we see marvellous thing. We stand off, you understand. But we use *télescope* — glass, glass! We see this thing *dans le ciel*. It gives *feu* — fire? *Quatre ou cinq vaisseaux sont finis. Merveilleux! Henri, Claude, voici l'homme du ballon! Aù est le vin?*"

Kieron was dazed. Suddenly, men were shaking him by the hand, clapping him on the back.

"Monsieur Kieron," said Captain Girod, "forgive me. I return the sword of a brave man. We are honoured by your presence on the *Marie-France*."

Kieron took the sword. It felt good in his hand.

"*Messieurs*," said Captain Girod, "*je vous presente un homme de vaillance. À votre santé, Monsieur Kieron.*"

Miraculously wine and glasses had appeared, brought by a fourth man from below. The Frenchmen raised their glasses and drank deep.

Then Kieron also raised his glass. "*Monsieur le capitaine*, I thank you for saving my life."

"Monsieur Kieron, it was — I say it right? — my pleasure. I am speak of this in years to come."

The wine tasted good. No sooner was Kieron's glass

empty than it was refilled. He swallowed the good red wine of France and felt a tingling in his limbs.

"Captain Girod," he said thickly, "can you set me upon the coast of Britain?"

"Monsieur Kieron, name your destination." He laughed. "For you, my friend, I will sail the *Marie-France* even under the guns of *l'Amiral Mort*."

Kieron smiled faintly. "I wish only to land two or three kilometres east of Little Hampton."

"Come below, *monsieur*, where it is warm and light. You shall drink more wine while I look at the charts ... We are many kilometres from land, you see. It will take time. I do not think you may put ashore much before daylight. It will be *dangereux* — dangerous."

"I am familiar with danger."

"*Pardon. Je suis un fou. Monsieur*, come below. Rest."

"Captain, I would like to stay on deck a while. I would like to look at the stars."

"*Ah, les étoiles!*" Captain Girod shook his head uncomprehendingly. "My ship is yours, *monsieur. Excusez-moi*."

Kieron stayed on deck for a time and gazed at the night sky. Truly, it was very beautiful. Truly, he had never before realised quite how beautiful those remote points of light were in the mystery that men called the firmament.

Suddenly he began to laugh. He began to laugh because he had just discovered that he was longer indifferent to his own fate. But a short time ago, he had not cared whether he lived or died. Now he knew that he greatly wished to live. To look at the sky on other nights such as this. To construct more balloons and other machines of the air. To hold Petrina close in love and desire. To see his son grow tall ... To live ... To create and to remember ... To suffer and take joy ... To live!

He laughed loud and helplessly. Perhaps it is the wine, he told himself, feeling fire in his limbs. I am unused to French wine. But he knew it was not the wine. It was — it was ... What was it? The life force! That was a good phrase. He felt he had just invented it. The life force.

The force that draws flowers and crops out of the earth, that makes women beautiful and causes men — some men — to lift up their eyes to the stars.

"Some day," said Kieron, gazing at Sirius, the brightest star of all, "my children's children will reach out towards you. Think not, bright star, that you are beyond the reach of men."

Again he laughed, thinking how a small French ship had found him, on a great ocean, thinking how chance had brought him back from the dead. "By the hammer," he laughed, "the astrologer Marcus will yet confound all disbelievers."

Down below, as Captain Girod consulted his charts, he heard the mad bursts of laughter. He shrugged. It was known that the English had always been a little mad. Clearly this one, who had himself challenged the might of an armed fleet, was much afflicted.

16

CAPTAIN GIROD WAS as good as his word. He took the *Marie-France* close in to the south coast of Britain almost exactly three kilometres east of Little Hampton. The stars were fading and the sky was turning grey as Kieron clambered over the side of the French ship and prepared to row ashore in his small boat.

"*Monsieur,*" said Captain Girod, "we have been honoured by your company. Please accept this small gift and remember us with affection." He handed Kieron a flask of *eau de vie.* "Some day, I think, our nations will again work together. You will drink to that?"

"I will drink to that. Captain Girod, you have saved my life, but I have no gift to offer."

"Monsieur Kieron, we already have your gift. *Merde, alors.* It was *formidable. Un homme du ciel contre les bateaux de l'Amiral Mort.* Please, we shall tell our children's children of this thing. We have your gift. *Soyez tranquille.* Rest easy."

"I beg one more favour, Captain. Give me oil. Give me the means of making fire."

"*Pourquoi?* You cannot make the attack from this small boat."

"No, *monsieur.* I wish to burn my boat when I have landed. It has served me well. No other shall use it."

"Monsieur Kieron, I comprehend."

A member of the crew brought a large bottle of oil, some waste cloth and a lighted candle-cup. Kieron stored the candle-cup carefully in his boat so that the breeze would not extinguish the flame.

"Goodbye, Captain, and thank you. May you have a safe voyage home."

"*Bonne chance, monsieur.* We salute your audacity. It will be remembered."

Kieron pulled for the shore. He could only see it dimly, but it seemed to be deserted. There was little swell, but the tide was with him. As he rowed, the *Marie-France* swung slowly round and faded slowly like a ghost in the pre-dawn light.

By the time he had beached, the red rim of the sun had risen above the horizon. Kieron hauled his boat clear of the water. The soft sand felt good beneath his feet. He was amazed at how good it felt. But perhaps that was because he had not expected to walk on dry land again.

He looked along the shore both ways. It was totally deserted. He sat down for a while, picking up handfuls of sand and letting it trickle between his fingers. A sense of desolation grew oddly upon him. He felt that he was the last man alive.

After a time, his mind returned to practicalities. The candle-cup was still burning. He made a small pile of the waste cloth he had been given, then he searched for fragments of flotsam. He found a few splintered pieces of ships' timber, not large, but enough to make a small bonfire with the waste cloth. He poured oil over it and placed the candle-cup beneath a strip of the soaked rag. The flames leaped high. For a moment or two he stood warming himself, realising that he had felt very cold.

Then he recollected the purpose of the bonfire. He turned *Mistress Fitzalan's Revenge* upside down and kicked repeatedly at the thin strips of wood until they were stove in. Then he lifted the wreckage of the boat and let it fall upon the bonfire.

Sparks rose mightily. The wet timbers sizzled and crackled and steamed and smoked. Finally, they burst into flame; and *Mistress Fitzalan's Revenge* was at last consumed by the very element she had carried to destroy the vessels of Admiral Death.

Kieron waited until all the wood of the small boat had been reduced to embers. By which time, the sun was well clear of the horizon. He looked at the glowing ashes and the fragments of charred wood. Soon the incoming tide would reach them, and all traces of the boat would be washed away for ever... This, too, had been a funeral pyre.

Now it was time to return to the living. The sky was blue and it was going to be another fine day. Kieron judged it time to strike quickly inland, lest he encounter any of the freebooters abroad early. He gazed westward, along the beach and out to sea; but he could see no sign of them or their vessels. Which was of no great significance, since the coast curved, and Little Hampton was out of sight.

Kieron left the shore and took to the fields and moorland, passing near the ruins of several abandoned cottages. There was still the smell of smoke and death about them. No doubt they had recently suffered the ministrations of the freebooters.

Although it would have been easier to head directly for Arundel, Kieron judged this not to be a wise course. After the onslaught from the air, Admiral Death may well have decided to march inland, exacting retribution from any who had been so bold as to attempt to reoccupy their damaged towns and villages. Better by far to make a wearisome detour through fields and woodland, perhaps eventually coming to the Misery from the east or the north.

If Kieron had not been persuaded to sleep aboard the *Marie-France*, at least he had been persuaded to eat. Captain Girod had given him good bread, and sliced meat, and Normandy cheese. But that was hours ago; and now he felt hungry once more. He had nothing to eat, but he did have the flask of *eau de vie*. He took out its stopper and drank. The fluid set his limbs on fire and took away the pains of hunger; but it did not seem to cloud his mind. Rather, it appeared to bring clarity of thought and to supply energy.

Kieron strode rapidly across the long stretches of grassland, sword in one hand, flask in the other. Occasionally, he sang songs, occasionally he drank. Always he looked for signs of men. But the world, it seemed, was deserted. Perhaps it was no sad jest to imagine himself as the last man alive.

Now he could see the towers and battlements of Arundel castle. There was no obvious sign of activity. But he stayed well to the east of the castle and travelled north. He felt desperately tired and very thirsty. Even the *eau de vie* could no longer stave off the hunger pains.

It seemed to be a warm morning. The weather was kind. How pleasant it would be to sit down and rest a while. He was greatly tempted; but then he recollected that the only safe place to rest would be the Misery, and preferably in the arms of Petrina.

Somehow he managed to keep himself moving. With luck, and if he used his remaining energy carefully, he would reach the Misery in less than two hours, perhaps even in little more than one.

The sun had already passed its zenith by the time he reached the encampment. He approached it from the north and wondered why he was not challenged by sentinels or watch men. Kentigern, it seemed, was getting careless.

Kieron felt weak. He could not see very clearly, he could not now think very clearly, and his gait was none too steady. For want of food, he had emptied the flask of *eau de vie* given him by Captain Girod. But his wits still functioned, if slowly. When he entered the clearing, he stood swaying and taking in the scene with much amazement. Not many people remained, and there were several faces he did not recognise. Everyone seemed to be frantically busy making bundles of their belongings and loading them upon horse-drawn or hand-drawn carts.

Kentigern was there, he saw, supervising the loading of the carts. Petrina was there also. They were so busy that they did not notice him at first. He staggered forward. Petrina was the first to turn her head.

"Kieron! Kieron, my beloved! I knew you were not dead!" She ran to him, held him close, supported him, kissed his face and hair. "I knew you would come. They said you had fallen into the sea from a great height. But I knew you would come."

"Forgive me, I'm drunk," was all he could say. "No food. Much *eau de vie*. Forgive me."

Great shouts went up from the people. "Kieron!" "The Cloud Walker has returned!" "Kieron is here!" "Ludd protect us, he has risen from the dead!"

Kentigern came forward. Kieron felt his knees giving way but Petrina held him, strangely poured strength back into him.

"What is this?" he said thickly. "Where are the rest of our people? Who are these I do not know? What is happening?" He raised the sword he still held, the sword that seemed now a part of himself.

Kentigern said: "Rest easy, Kieron. Put your sword down. The battle is over. These are slaves escaped from the shattered vessels of Admiral Death. They help us to return to our homes, that is all ... I did not think that you would live. Through the glass, you were seen to fall into the sea from a great height." He shrugged. "But you, I think, are a man to confound the Devil."

"It was not I, but Aylwin who fell."

"So. Aylwin, who was your friend, was also touched by greatness ... Kieron, you destroyed five vessels, so the escaped slaves tell us, and blew a leg off Admiral Death who is now near to that condition signified by his name. The freebooters have departed from Little Hampton. Perchance, they did not know that there was only one shark of the sky ... So we return to our homes, Kieron. We shall rebuild the town and take some precautions against a repetition of recent disasters. This meets with your approval?"

"I am content," Kieron managed to say. "I will live in

Master Hobart's house, and, to please a certain astrologer, I will beget three sons."

Then, despite Petrina's support, he fell unconscious.

The people in the Misery drew close, watched Petrina lift his head, press it to her breast.

"Look upon this man," said Kentigern. "He is but eighteen years old, and he was known as a fool. Yet he has delivered us. I, Kentigern, kneel before him. Let no one stand at this time unless he presumes to be a better man."

The people in the Misery knelt before Kieron. Then, after a space, they made a bed for him on one of the carts. Petrina lay beside him, stroking his white hair. Then they loosed the horses from the cart, and ten men drew him to Master Hobart's house.

17

FOR THE NEXT few days, every man, woman and child
who had returned to the town of Arundel worked throughout every hour of daylight and through many of the hours
of darkness, also. Walls, doors, windows, even roofs were
to be mended, new furniture and furnishings had to be
sought or constructed; food had to be got; tools and
weapons had to be fashioned; the sick and wounded had
to be cared for; and a start had to be made on repairing
the damage done at the castle.

Kentigern, in the absence of other authority, assumed
responsibility for the seigneurie. He sent messengers east
and west to discover if Admiral Death's entire fleet had
quit the southern coast of England or had only sought
refuge farther from the source of the fire-balloon. He sent
messengers with the news of the result of Kieron's attack
to the grand seigneurs at London. He organised companies
of men to clear the streets of the stinking corpses of freebooters, to mend fences and walls, to round up stray cattle,
to scythe the last few fields of corn, to hunt for deer,
pheasants, rabbits.

During the first day of the return, Kieron was the only
man in the seigneurie who rested. Master Hobart's house
had been little damaged and needed little attention. Men
fitted a new door and a new window quietly while he
slept. Women brought rich brocade for curtains — sent by
Kentigern from the castle — and children laid bundles of
wild flowers by the doorstep, as if at a shrine.

Kieron slept entirely throughout the first day and the
first night. He awoke refreshed on the following morning

— refreshed and very hungry, and filled with the unquenchable vigour of youth. He breakfasted greedily; and the breakfast he was given was fit for a seigneur: oatmeal porridge with cream and honey, cold pheasants' breast with pickle and new baked bread, preserve of strawberries and a bottle of golden wine called hock, sent from the castle cellars with the compliments of Kentigern.

Kieron ate all the porridge, disposed of the breasts of two fine cock pheasants, and drank half the bottle of wine. Then he held Petrina close to him and stroked her hair.

"I am alive," he said wonderingly. "I am still alive."

"And you must remain alive for some time," said Petrina, "if you are to fulfil your promise."

"What did I promise?"

"To beget three sons." She laughed. "If only to make an honest man of the astrologer Marcus."

"I will keep my promise," he asserted. "I have need of sons. To reconquer the air will take more strength than I possess."

Petrina's face became grave.

"You do not smile?" he asked. "You used to be amused by the strange notions of Kieron-head-in-the-air."

"I thought they were idle fancies. I did not then know the terrible reality."

He kissed her. "Be of good cheer, Petrina. I came back, did I not?"

"Yes."

"And I will always come back. Even though the sky is my true home."

She gave him a sad smile. "Your true home ... You must know that it is a frightening thought for me ... Ah, well, I must make the best of it. I am lucky to have you ... No one calls you Kieron-head-in-the-air any more. Did you know that?"

"What do they call me, then?"

"The Cloud Walker. Since your foolish dream became a terrible reality, they laugh no more. They are proud of you. They ask after your health. They ask what the Cloud Walker will do next."

Kieron laughed. "That is easy to answer. Having rested and eaten well and known the comfort of his wife, he will go forth to help restore life to our little town."

"Be not surprised at how men receive you," Petrina called after him. "There are some, even, who think you have risen from the dead."

It was a dull, overcast morning, but the air was warm. Kieron found much activity in the High Street. Carpenters and plasterers were at work. Women cleaned steps with chalk stone and swilled pavements with water. Everywhere there was much bustle as people strove to make their town look as if the freebooters had never been.

Kieron found himself greeted with great deference. Men twice his age, who would formerly have dismissed him with a shrug or a condescending smile, touched their hats or hair and addressed him as Master or Sir. Young men of his own age, with whom he had been wont to exchange insults or jokes, looked upon him with awe, vied for his attention. No one seemed inclined to let him help at menial tasks. Kieron felt alone and uncomfortable. He was greatly relieved when he saw Kentigern approach, presumably upon his round of inspection.

"Well, Kentigern. The town recovers rapidly, I see. Do you have news of the freebooters?"

"Ay, Master Kieron, I have news. Better news, perhaps than we dared hope for. Admiral Death survived your attentions but briefly. He perished, I am told, in much agony in a freebooter's vessel anchored off the Isle of Wight. With his passing, the command of the freebooters disintegrated. They quarrelled among themselves. Slave crews rebelled. Some freebooter ships fired upon each other. But, more important, they have all left these shores." He grinned. "No doubt the story of the attack of the shark of the sky grew with the telling. They had no means of knowing that the same dreadful assault would not be made again."

"Well, then," said Kieron, "*Mistress Fitzalan's Revenge* has justified her name."

"More than that," said Kentigern. "Sir, I envy you. Mistress Alyx Fitzalan has been avenged mightily."

Kieron was at a loss. "It was not for her alone, you understand."

"Master Kieron, let us not speak any more of these things. There are words best left unsaid ... Now to more immediate matters. I have inspected the records of lineage, mercifully untouched by the freebooters. Somewhere in the Americas, there is a Seigneur Howard who will undoubtedly inherit from Seigneur Fitzalan. But until and if Seigneur Howard returns to this island, do I have your consent to remain as bailiff of the castle and steward of the seigneurie?"

Kieron was confused. "You do not need my consent."

Kentigern laughed. "Master Kieron, forgive me, in matters practical you are still a fool. I did not save the seigneurie. You did. The people will follow you to the death. If you wish to assume the duties of administration, you are welcome. They are heavy enough, and the burden does not please me."

"I know nothing of such matters," said Kieron hurriedly. "Do not confuse me. You are the bailiff of Arundel. You have my allegiance."

"I am truly relieved to know it," confessed Kentigern. "If men did not know that you accepted my authority, there would doubtless be trouble. A true seigneur they would not question, but a bailiff ..." He shrugged.

"Here is my hand on it, then."

"I take it in friendship." Kentigern held out his own. "What will you do now that the freebooters have gone? Until Seigneur Howard reveals himself, or until the Grand Council appoints a surrogate seigneur, there will be little work for a master artist."

"I do not wish to paint, except for my own pleasure."

Kentigern stroked his chin thoughtfully. "So. Then my task is easier ... By the authority I hold until relieved, as bailiff of the seigneurie of Arundel for the late Seigneur Fitzalan and his heirs or assigns, I now appoint you, Master Kieron Joinerson, Warden of the Coast and Captain of Aerial Warfare. These posts to bring in fee one thousand schilling each per year, payable in portions on the quarter days ... Can you and your family live upon two thousand schilling, Kieron?"

Two thousand schilling! It was far more money than he had ever seen. It seemed a princely fee. Kieron's father had never earned more than two hundred schilling a year in all his life.

Kieron was overwhelmed. "Two thousand schilling is more than enough," he managed to say. "But what am I to do for all this money?"

"Why, man, you are to construct hot-air balloons. What else? You are to make sure that never again shall we be so punished by the scum of the oceans. You are to defend us from neighbouring seigneuries; for it is certain that, with the death of Seigneur Fitzalan, there will be those who cast greedy eyes upon Arundel. Possession, you will recall, is nine points of the law. Well, Kieron, will you defend us?"

"To the best of my ability."

Kentigern laughed heartily. "That is more than a guarantee. For years to come, Kieron, your name alone will be worth more than a hundred well-armed horsemen ... Of course, the seigneurie will pay for all the arms, materials and supplies you require. Also, men will be trained according to your instructions. Does this meet with your approval?"

"It meets with my approval," said Kieron weakly.

"Well, then, my friend. Go home and devise plans. Send me a reckoning of what you require in men and materials. Make us invincible, that is all."

18

FOR THE SECOND time, Kieron was awakened with a sword-point at his chest. Petrina, lying by his side, opened her eyes and screamed at what she saw by the light of a lantern and the pre-dawn greyness that crept through the window. She saw two armoured men, wearing tabards on which were blazoned the device of the Inquisitor General of the Luddite Church. One man held the lantern, the other held the sword.

"You are Kieron Joinerson, lately apprenticed to Master Hobart, the painter?"

"He is the one," said a dark, cowled figure standing by the doorway.

Kieron recognised the voice of Brother Lemuel.

"Silence, brother," said the man with the sword. "You have done your work. Let him speak for himself."

Petrina desperately covered her nakedness. The night had been one of passion and desire. Kieron tried to clear his head and concentrate. He gazed at the heraldic device upon the tabards: a golden hammer upon a field of azure above symbolic flames worked in thread of gold.

"You are Kieron Joinerson? Speak fellow. Else I loosen your tongue."

"I am Kieron Joinerson."

"Then dress quickly. Your presence is required in the great hall of the castle."

"My wife?"

"We have no instructions concerning your wife. Hurry, man! The Holy Office does not brook delay."

"What is the cause of this intrusion?"

"You will know soon enough, if you do not know already. Hurry man!"

Kieron kissed Petrina. "Rest easy, my love. Do not offend them. Kentigern will deal with this nonsense. That I swear."

He climbed out of bed and put on his clothes. Petrina lay under the sheets and blankets, shaking and trying to stifle her weeping, cursing her nakedness.

When Kieron was dressed, the sword was held towards his belly while his arms were tied behind his back.

"Petrina, my sister," said Brother Lemuel with a gentle voice, "in this time of trial, do you require the consolations of Holy Church?"

Petrina raised her head from the blankets. "Get from my presence!" she hissed. "Go elsewhere and corrupt children. After this day's work no woman in the seigneurie will look upon you but to spit."

Kieron laughed. He laughed with joy to find that his wife had such spirit. He was rewarded by a buffet in the mouth from the lantern-holder. His lip bled, and he savoured the salt taste.

"Sir, I will remember that you struck a bound man. There will be a reckoning."

The man with the lantern laughed. "Ay, there will be a reckoning, Master Kieron. When the flames leap high, there will be a reckoning. March!"

Kieron was led out into the street. More armed men were waiting. They surrounded him, as if fearful that the townsfolk might move to release him. But the sun had not yet shown itself, and the people of Arundel still slept after their heavy labours. Whoever had planned this event had planned well.

But as Kieron was marched to the castle, his spirits rose. Kentigern would surely have enough authority to stop this idiocy.

At the castle, the strength of the Inquisitor General's forces was made more apparent. Kieron saw foot soldiers guarding the castle gate; and in the yard there were ten or more horses showing signs of recent and hard travel.

Kieron was taken into the great hall, where lamps and a fire burned, and where Brother Hildebrand awaited him together with officers of the Inquisitor General. There also stood Kentigern. Kieron was amazed to note that his hands were bound also.

"Good morning, Kieron," said Brother Hildebrand. "You see now to what a condition your persistent heresy has brought you."

"Good morning, brother," said Kieron caustically. "Your task being what it is, I do not wonder that you come like a thief in the night."

The soldier who had struck him in the bedroom struck him once more. Kieron reeled from the blow. "I will remember your bravery, fellow," Kieron grated. "Pray that I am never unbound."

He turned to Kentigern. "Did you not set watch men?"

Kentigern gave a mirthless smile. "They were not instructed to guard us against the Luddite Church, Kieron. I truly regret the error. The freebooters at least struck as our enemies. These presume to be our friends."

"We shall pray greatly for you," said Brother Hildebrand. "Ludd's will be done. Whatever may befall, rest assured that we shall save your immortal souls."

"With such friends," said Kieron, "we have no need of enemies."

"Silence, fellow!"

A man stood forward. He wore the habit of a neddy; but round his neck there hung a silver chain, and from the chain a small golden hammer was suspended. He carried a scroll which he opened and from which he then read.

"To Kieron, apprentice of Master Hobart, painter, and to Kentigern, bailiff of Seigneur Fitzalan of the seigneurie of Arundel, greetings. I, Xavier, Inquisitor General of the Holy Luddite Church, commend your souls to Ludd, and require the servants of the Church to convey you to the

Sacred College of Nedd Ludd in the city of London where you shall be tried for diverse heresies and sundry treasons. It is my wish that my beloved brother Constant, Steward of the Inquisition, shall have regard for your comfort and safety upon the journey and shall bring you in safety to judgment, which shall be given by the Inquisitor General upon the advice of ten High Stewards and such persons as may speak in your favour."

Kentigern laughed. "They mean to burn us, Kieron. It is humorous, is it not? You destroyed the freebooters with your hot-air balloon, and I gave you some small assistance. They mean to burn us. That is droll — if not unexpected."

"By the hammer, I would like to see them try to burn us if the trial were held in this seigneurie."

"By the hammer, Kieron, you have the truth of it!" shouted Kentigern. He turned to the Steward Constant, who had just read from the scroll. "It is an ancient right, Steward, granted to all men, that, if accused of any crime, including heresy, they may choose to be tried in their own seigneurie and in the presence of their people."

Constant gave an unpleasant laugh. "It is true, fellow, that a man may choose to be tried in his own seigneurie; but first he must plead such choice in the presence of his seigneur. You have no seigneur. Holy Church, as always, acts within the law and maintains the law . . . Now, it is a long ride to London. Do you go peaceably, or do my officers knock you on the head and draw you like meat in a cart?"

Kieron and Kentigern looked at each other in dismay.

"It is better to go peaceably," said Kieron. "A man with his wits about him still has the dignity of a man."

"Bind their mouths," said Constant. "We must be away before sunrise, else this confused and misguided citizenry may note and dispute our passage."

Cloths were placed over the mouths of Kieron and Kentigern. Then, with armed men escorting them, they were led out into the castle yard, where saddled horses were now waiting.

Kieron glanced hopefully at the sky. But there was much low cloud, and light would be slow in coming. By the time that people were abroad and the situation made known to them, a troop of horsemen could be many kilometres to the north. He thought of Petrina. When he had been hustled out of his bed chamber, Brother Lemuel had remained. Guards also had been left at the door of Hobart's house. He hoped no harm would come to her. But it would be a terrible thing for her to live the rest of her life as the widow of a man burned for heresy. And there was the child ... How would the son of the Cloud Walker feel when he was old enough to understand the fate of his father?

"Have the prisoners well mounted," said Constant. "We ride hard. I am entrusted with their safety. I have no wish to explain a broken neck to the Inquisitor General. Also," he laughed, "they may yet prove innocence."

A soldier, helping Kieron to mount his horse, grunted, coughed, opened his eyes wide with surprise and fell to the ground. In the half-light, Kieron saw an arrow shaft protruding from his back.

"Let no one move," said a voice, "unless he wishes to follow this one rapidly to eternity."

"Mount!" shouted Constant. "Mount, everyone! Let us away!"

Two more men tried to force Kieron into the saddle. Both died.

The Steward Constant stood quite still, peering in the half-light, seeing no one. So did the rest of his party.

"You who are hidden," called Constant, "know that I am a Steward of the office of the Inquisitor General and that I lawfully take these men to give account of themselves in his presence. Justice shall be done."

"You who are not hidden," answered the voice, "rest easy. Do not move. Justice shall indeed be done. I will count three. Upon the count of three, all men bearing weapons will let them fall, or they will die. One ... Two ... Three."

There was a great clatter as swords, daggers, cross-bows and bolts fell to the ground. Kieron looked joyfully about him. The light was gaining strength. He could now vaguely discern figures on the battlements, men crouched by the stables, men standing shoulder to shoulder with drawn bows in the castle gateway.

"That is most sensible," said the voice. "Now we may talk." A man stepped out of the shadows to be revealed as Isidor. Two more men followed him, cutting the ropes that bound Kieron and Kentigern and tearing the cloth bindings from their mouths.

"You come opportunely," said Kentigern.

"You must thank Mistress Petrina for that," said Isidor solemnly. "I am told she broke a chamber pot over the head of a prating neddy; and then, disguised in his habit, left the guarded house to raise the alarm."

Kieron burst out laughing. "Miracles come aplenty. Two boys and a hot-air balloon rout the freebooters, and the power of the Luddite Church is broken by a chamber pot. Ludd, it seems, does not always favour the big battalions."

Kentigern rubbed his wrists and looked at the Steward Constant. "This creature was about to take us to London for a burning."

"We knew their plans," said Isidor. "We found one who talked with much enthusiasm and a dagger at his throat ... I decided not to lead men into the castle, not knowing if they would kill you in the mêlée."

"An excellent decision. But they would not have killed. Such tricksters need to have their crimes approved in writing." He turned to the Luddite officers and soldiers, who had now been lined up by more of Isidor's followers. "Well, fellows, you came not openly to perform your task but under cover of darkness like common rogues. You did not bring your arms when we needed them to drive out the invader. It seems your masters were not overly concerned with the fate of our women and children, having more important matters to consider — such as the dreadful crime of conspiring to construct a hot-air balloon. I have ever shown respect for the Church and its teachings, even when I thought them severe. But now that I have seen how the Luddite Church cares for its flock, I say we have no need of such madness in this seigneurie."

His words were followed by a great roar of approval. Kieron looked round. The light was gaining strength. It seemed now that all the grown men and many of the women of Arundel were assembled in the castle yard. He saw Petrina and smiled at her.

Kentigern confronted the Steward. He snapped the silver chain that hung round Constant's neck and let the small golden hammer drop at his feet. He put his foot upon it and ground it with his heel. He took the scroll from Constant's hand and slowly tore in into pieces. The Steward stood pale, motionless, surmising perhaps that his last hour had come.

"So, master champion of Holy Writ, you have heard the voice of the people — the free people of Arundel. Many have lost wives, husbands, sons, daughters, while such as you meditated upon the wickedness of heretical acts. I doubt that any man or woman present would shed a tear if we hanged a dozen Luddites before breaking our fast."

Again there was a great roar of approval.

"But do not tremble, sir Steward. We are civilised folk — until we are greatly wronged. So you may return to your Inquisitor General in London and give him our thanks for the fine horses he has sent us and for the arms. Say they arrived late, but no matter. Say also that Kentigern sends his regrets, but chooses to remain bailiff of the seigneurie of Arundel until an inheritor is recognised. Say also that Master Kieron Joinerson is too busy to attend his trial for heresy, having been appointed Warden of the Coast, Captain of Aerial Defence and — most recently — Master of Machines. Say finally that, if any force be raised against us, if any Luddite mission again enters this seigneurie, we shall reply most dreadfully with fire from the air and with machines of destruction beyond the imaginings of such as you ... You will remember these words?"

"I — I will remember them," Constant managed to say, though his voice was very small.

"Go, then. Six hours from now, dogs and men on horseback shall be sent after you. It will go ill if they find you upon the lands of the seigneurie." Kentigern turned to the crowd. "Do I speak for you?"

"By the hammer —" shouted someone, then changed his mind. "By the reach of the Cloud Walker, you speak for us." There were cheers and much laughter.

"A last reckoning," called Kentigern. "Where are they who brought vermin in our midst?"

The two neddies, Lemuel and Hildebrand were pushed forward. Lemuel wore only his stockings and a long undershirt. There was blood upon his head and an expression of great mortification upon his face. Hildebrand had the look of one who expected sudden death.

Kentigern stared hard at them both. "You, I cannot find it in my heart to forgive nor your deeds to forget. You were of our people, your parents, whom you dishonour, raised you in the seigneurie, you saw the terrible destruction we endured. And yet, with pious words, you sought to work more mischief. It is my judgment that chains shall be set upon your hands and legs for a twelve-month. You shall sleep on straw in the stables, and you shall be any man's labourers. If you attempt to escape we shall hunt you with dogs. Be thankful that you live, fellows. Our justice is more gentle than yours would have been."

Kentigern faced his people. "My friends, I am not your seigneur; and likely it will be many years before one sits in the castle once more. But I will do my best for the seigneurie. That is all I can say."

"It is enough!" someone shouted. "We will have no strangers now. You know us and we know you. Raise hands those who accept Kentigern."

There was much shouting and cheering, as a forest of hands rose high.

"Well, then," said Kentigern gaily, "I am overwhelmed, being too much of a coward to challenge the will of the people . . . Not many days ago I was in a sad humour, being half convinced that the world was ending. Then the Cloud Walker came to me with wild talk of a hot-air balloon with which he would attack our enemies. He was mad, of course."

The crowd roared with laughter.

"But his madness was infectious, it seems . . . And, my friends, was it not an inspired madness? The world we knew has ended, a world in which it was a mortal sin for a man to devise something that would help his fellow men. But the Cloud Walker has given us the opportunity to build a new world. Shall we build that new world, or shall we return to the old ways?"

"The new!" they shouted. "Let us build the new!"

"I hear your answer," said Kentigern. "Well, my friends, set these creatures who came against us back on the road to London. Then go to your homes and eat well, for there is much hard work ahead for all."

As the crowd dispersed, and the officers of the Inquisitor General were jeered on their way, Petrina came to Kieron's side. He put his arm round her shoulders. "It was a heavy chamber pot?" he asked.

"It was a satisfyingly heavy chamber pot." She laughed. "I had no time to remove the contents."

Kieron turned to Kentigern. "I did not know you had such eloquent words in you."

"Nor did I," confessed Kentigern. "Kieron, I am in your debt. I greatly fear that your strange ideas have made a man of me."

"A man," observed Kieron, "must either fall or rise in adversity."

"Well said. But now we have many problems. Likely, the Luddite Church will try to reassert its authority. How much time do you need to construct hot-air balloons?"

"How many?"

"Let us say five."

Kieron was aghast. "Five? You want me to make five?"

"Let us hope for the best and prepare for the worst," said Kentigern.

"Can you give me a hundred men?"

"Yes."

"And a thousand square metres of linen and paper?"

"Yes — if I have to send riders abroad, and strip every woman in the seigneurie of her petticoats."

"Well, then, in five days you shall have five hot-air balloons, armed and ready to defend the seigneurie."

"That is better than I hoped. I think it will take the Luddites at least eight days to raise a force against us — if they have the stomach for it."

Petrina shivered and said: "Kieron, come. The sun has risen. We must eat."

"My love, I am too busy. There is much to think about, much to do."

Kentigern cleared his throat. "Cloud Walker, I command you in little. But it is necessary that you remain alive and in good health. Must I send men to hold you while you are fed?"

Kieron laughed. "You are a hard master, Kentigern. But I have a sterner mistress. I live, now, in fear of chamber pots. I will eat."

19

By the time he was twenty-eight years old, Kieron had become a legend and had achieved the reputation of being immortal. He had broken both legs, both arms and had sustained other injuries that would have consigned many lesser men to the grave. He had endured all this because of his obsession with the conquest of the air. Hot-air balloons he had left behind him. These were now the province of his less-gifted apprentices and craftsmen. His present obsession was with sailplanes, machines that would glide through the air like birds.

The Luddite Church had never again challenged the seigneurie of Arundel. The Luddite Church was in decline. As the news of Kieron's successful attack upon the forces of Admiral Death had spread quickly through neighbouring seigneuries and more slowly through the rest of the island's seigneuries, followed hard by the news that the Luddite Church had been proscribed in Arundel, men of intelligence everywhere began to think about these matters. The Church had been made to look ridiculous by its furtive attempt to capture the Cloud Walker — the only man who had known how to deal with the freebooters — and charge him with heresy. More, the Church had not only been made to look ridiculous, it had become ridiculous — showing plainly that it was concerned more with dogma than with the welfare of the people.

For centuries the Luddites, drawing their inspiration from the fates that had overtaken the First Men and the Second Men, had maintained their power by fear, authoritarianism, and punishment. They had attempted, as it were, to freeze history, to maintain a society that neither declined nor improved. They had attempted to imprison the spirit of man like a fly in amber. Countless ingenious, inventive and creative people, attempting to improve their own lot and that of their fellow creatures, had been imprisoned, tortured, burned in order to maintain the doctrine that machines were anathema. But a strange and wonderful machine had been necessary to defeat Admiral Death; and the people of the seigneurie of Arundel had delivered their verdict upon the teachings of the Church.

Men of intelligence dwelt upon these matters. Young men — ambitious and imaginative young men — throughout the country regarded the Cloud Walker with as much awe and reverence as their fathers and forefathers had regarded the Divine Boy. Many of the adventurous ones — young men with strange ideas and fanciful notions — broke their apprenticeships, left home and kith and kin, and journeyed to Arundel to seek service with the man who seemed to them to have opened the door to a new golden age. Some were recaptured by their masters or parents and were punished by their seigneurs or by the Church. But enough reached the Free Seigneurie, as they called it, to provide the Cloud Walker with an élite corps of young men with ideas.

He received them joyfully as brothers, sons, companions of the spirit. The best of them lived in his house, ate at his table, having free access to their beloved Cloud Walker. Kieron had long since fulfilled the prediction of the astrologer Marcus and had begotten three sturdy sons. Master Hobart's house had been considerably extended to accommodate wife, sons, and chosen apprentices in comfort. It was no longer just a house. It was a small university.

Petrina had grown beautiful with the years, even more opulent in her body, and immensely proud of her husband and her sons. She presided over her extensive household like a queen. Students competed for her smile and approval. No one but Kieron aspired to her love. Each time he experimented with a new flying machine, she held her breast tightly and tried vainly not to weep. When he was brought home in pain, she soothed him and ministered to him and gave him hope for the future.

Sometimes, she looked at the painting of *Mistress Fitzalan's Leap* that he had lovingly restored, his last act as a master painter. Sometimes she hated that slender, bright-eyed girl, sitting a horse so wonderfully between earth and sky. Sometimes she wept for her. Alyx Fitzalan had never known the joy of lying with her love, had never borne three sons.

Always, Petrina gave herself freely to Kieron — her mind, her spirit, her body. To her alone he was not the Cloud Walker. To her only he was a man who drove himself too hard, a lonely man whose tears and anguish and desire could only be released in the anonymity of darkness.

One day, when the wind was right, blowing steadily from the east, Kieron sat in the aeronaut's cage of his seventh sailplane. It lay upon the beach at Little Hampton, attached to a rope that would be drawn at his signal by eight good horses, the best that Kentigern could supply.

He sat thinking, waiting for the wind to stiffen. He was thinking of the six preceding sailplanes. The first one — no more than a pair of imitation bird wings with a central harness for a man — had actually left the ground but had turned over in flight. Kieron had been lucky to escape with a broken arm only. The second one, having two wings, one set above the other, had not even left the ground, having been shaken to pieces as it was drawn along the beach by a team of horses. The third one, shaped like a gull in gliding flight and made cunningly of wood and canvas, had risen beautifully, only to have its wings broken by the fierce pressure of air, so that Kieron had fallen like a stone into the sea and, having broken a leg, had only been saved from drowning by a devoted apprentice who was a great swimmer. The fourth and fifth sailplanes had been subtle variations upon the gull design. There was a gifted apprentice, Bruno of York, who had travelled on foot across the length and breadth of England to reach the Free Seigneurie. Bruno, like his master, was obsessed by flight and had greatly studied the aerial movements of such birds as the swift and the swallow. He spoke convincingly of air resistance and the importance of what he called smooth or streamed lines. He, though not yet twenty, unlike the other apprentices, did not fear to openly challenge the notions of his beloved master — for which Kieron held him in great affection.

According to Bruno, the ideal form of an aerial machine would be obtained by combining all that was vital in the wing pattern of a gliding bird with a stream-lined body derived from the shape of one of the fast swimming fishes. He had even persuaded Kieron to spend half a day by the banks of the Arun, watching trout glide through the water, controlling their movements with a flicker of the tail.

So the design of the fourth and fifth sailplanes had been changed according to Bruno's requirements for streamed lines. The fourth sailplane had risen well from the beach, but had proved impossible to control. After a flight of perhaps two hundred metres, it had buried its fish-nose in the sand and had thrown Kieron head over heels through the air to land most painfully upon his back.

But, with Bruno's assistance, he had made the best heavier-than-air flight so far. Together, they laboured on the design of the fifth sailplane. Longer, more slender wings. Smoother, streamed lines. A fish-tail, which could be moved a little from side to side by the aeronaut pulling ropes.

This one flew almost a kilometre, till the fabric was ripped from one of its wings and once more Kieron broke a limb.

The sixth sailplane was an even more ambitious version of the fifth. It was almost entirely Bruno's own design. Besides a moving tail-fin, he had devised thin, moveable flaps on the wings, and had so arranged matters that the aeronaut could control the movements of the wing-flaps or tail-fin by pushing and pulling wooden bars.

It was a beautiful machine, long tapering wings; slender rounded body. Sleek as a fish, light as a great bird. Bruno pleaded to be allowed to make the first flight. The other apprentices were awed by his temerity. Hitherto, the Cloud Walker had always been the first.

But, thought Kieron, why should not Bruno enjoy his own triumph — if, indeed, there were a triumph to enjoy?

So, on a bright morning, Bruno sat in the tiny aeronaut's basket built between the wings, tested his controls, glanced nervously back at the small tail-wings and the tail-fin, upon the design of which he had lavished much thought and care, smiled at Kieron, and gave the signal to the horsemen who would draw the sailplane on its wooden wheels along the beach, until it gained enough speed to rise.

The sailplane rose from the beach much faster than Kieron had anticipated. It rose beautifully, smoothly, confidently, the rope that held it to the horses dropping cleanly from the iron hook in the machine's nose. Bruno seemed to know instinctively how to handle the sailplane. It was more than fifty metres high when a sudden gust of wind seemed to snatch at it with nimble fingers and fling it aloft. The sudden lift caught Bruno unawares, he was thrown out of his small basket; and, with a long despairing cry, he fell to earth, being killed instantly.

Now as Kieron sat in the cage of the seventh sailplane — substantially the same as Bruno's design but with larger tailplanes and with straps to fasten the aeronaut to his machine — he thought of the heavier-than-air machines that had failed and also of the brilliant young man who had given his life in the struggle to reconquer the air. Bruno had looked somewhat as Aylwin had looked many years ago; though Bruno's wits were much sharper than Aylwin's had been, and his passions were much stronger.

I have killed many enemies and only two friends, mused Kieron as he sat in his aeronaut's cage. I have been lucky.

The wind was good. The men on horseback seventy

metres ahead of the sailplane, looked round expectantly, awaiting the signal. Let them wait, let them mutter and curse, thought Kieron complacently. The wind will get better.

His mind turned to his other apprentices ... To Lachlan of Edinburgh, who had marched south with a tattered fragment of a book containing the precious knowledge of how to prepare a gas that was lighter than air. Lachlan swore that one day he would produce this gas in such quantities as to raise many balloons and allow them to remain aloft for ever ... To Torben, who had come from Norwich, determined to learn about hot-air balloons, and then determined to construct better ones than the Cloud Walker had made. He had succeeded, too. Torben of the quiet ways, the small voice and the great ambition. He had even constructed a hot-air balloon that had carried three men across the sea to the Nether Lands ... And then there was Levis of Colchester — Levis, the wild one, who made his own black powder and designed his own rockets and fired them into the sky as if he were taking part in a religious ceremony. Levis had already blown three fingers off one hand and made himself blind in an eye by premature explosions; and his aerial rockets, though spectacular, leaving trails of smoke and fire across the sky, were fit only for use as weapons to terrify and confound the enemy. Though, so far, the Free Seigneurie had encountered no other enemy, being perhaps too powerful, too resolute, and possessing many ingenious minds. Levis, the dreamer, disliked his rockets being taken for weapons. He dreamed always of a rocket that would one day reach out towards the stars ...

Kieron smiled, thinking of these young men and others. People called them, affectionately, the Cloud Walker's Fledglings. But would not such fledglings one day command the skies?

The sailplane quivered. The wind had strengthened. Boys holding the wing-tips shivered. The waiting men on horseback swore at their restive mounts and glanced frequently at Kieron; but none was brave enough to question the judgment of the Cloud Walker.

Kieron sighed, gave a last look around him, and raised his hand. Perhaps he would die, as Bruno had done. Perhaps not. But this day belonged to Bruno himself. Whatever happened, others would continue the work.

The horsemen saw the raised hand. The sailplane lurched forward, bouncing somewhat over uneven patches of sand. Once the left wing-tip came down nearly touching. That would have brought disaster. But Kieron moved a wing-flap and the sailplane righted itself. As the horsemen gathered speed, the machine became more stable. Kieron saw sand and sea rushing past him. Then suddenly there was no more bumping. Majestically, steeply, the sailplane rose. Not too steep, not too steep, thought Kieron, easing his tail-flap to turn a little from the wind. The sailplane began to swing smoothly in a wide arc. Kieron glanced down and saw that he must be fifty, perhaps sixty metres above the ground. He felt a slight jerk as the tow rope disengaged smoothly from its hook.

"Bruno," he said aloud into the wind, "we are airborne. You are right, boy, this is better than balloons. With craft such as these, we shall not drift with the wind. We shall truly sail the sky."

He brought the sailplane round in a great circle, knowing that he was already losing height and that he must endeavour to land smoothly on the beach. As the wings swung, he glimpsed the seigneurie of Arundel — a toy castle and a toy town in the morning sunlight. He thought of Petrina and his sons — and then the castle was lost to view, and he concentrated anxiously on the problems of flight.

He had practised the wing controls on models and with the sailplane tethered in a high wind. He had the feel of his craft. It seemed even to be an extension of his own body.

Slowly, patiently, he eased the descending sailplane until

it pointed along the beach, its tail and nose at the right attitude. Then he centred his controls.

Down below the horsemen sat like statues. If they did not move he would crash into them. They scattered — one man falling from his mount and being dragged somewhat by it.

The air whistled about Kieron's face. The sea and the shore seemed to rush towards him. There was a sickening bump as the wheels hit the sand, then the sailplane bounced a few metres into the air once more and came down sedately. As the speed lessened, one wing-tip touched the sand; and the sailplane swung violently round. But for his harness, Kieron would have been thrown out with some force. That was one important thing that had been learned from the death of Bruno.

The machine had stopped and all was well. Men and boys were running towards it. For a moment or two, he sat in silence, wishing that Bruno were with him.

"We have done it," he said softly. "Bruno, we have done it. We have flown more than a kilometre in a heavier-than-air machine. This is the beginning."

Suddenly he was aware of shouts, exclamations, cheers. And the world was about him once more.

POSTSCRIPTUM

KIERON LEANED BACK in his wheeled chair, knowing that he would rise from it no more, and was content. They had brought doctors to tend him and fuss about him; doctors who said that he must have no more excitement, that he must rest a while. He knew better than the doctors. He knew that soon he would rest eternally. He was content.

It was late spring. He leaned back in his chair in the castle rose garden, and sniffed the sweet scents that drifted to him on a light breeze. There was a bed of damask roses, gloriously golden in colour. A master gardener in France had bred the rose and, seeking to please the Cloud Walker, had called it *Madame Petrina*. There was also a bed of tiny white roses, bred by the castle's own master gardener and called simply *Alyx*.

Between the small white roses of *Alyx* and the full golden roses of *Madame Petrina*, Kieron, Seigneur of Arundel by consent of the people, First Holder of the Eagle's Wings by unanimous vote of the International Guild of Aeronauts, sat contentedly and remembered all that an old man should remember.

Kentigern was long dead. Kentigern who had been a good seigneur and a true friend for more than thirty years. Petrina was dead — dear warm Petrina. She had been dead how long? Not long. He could still feel the pain. Two of her sons also. The first — inevitably called Marcus — burned to death on his first voyage as navigator of a hydrogen airship. And the second, Aylwin, had died when his sailplane had been caught in a storm. Kieron was glad that hydrogen airships were finished. They were too dangerous. They had destroyed many good men. Now helium was the great lifter. He was glad also that the Germans and the French and the Americans and the Japanese were developing petroleum engines to power the sailplanes.

But such discoveries and inventions had come too late to save two of his sons. Not too late to save Jason, though. Jason was master of electrics on a helium-lifted dirigible capable of carrying two hundred people. Jason was safely airborne, flying about the world to places like Tokyo, Lima, New York, Johannesburg with all the assurance and confidence of a generation that accepted mastery of the air.

A great shadow passed over the rose garden. Without looking up, Kieron knew what it was. It was the daily, helium-filled airship from London to Rome. It always came over at this time. You could set a clock by it. Its propellers were powered by steam engines. Perhaps in a few years the petroleum engines would drive the great airships also.

Kieron fingered the red and white ribbon that hung round his neck and the Eagle's Wings, worked in iron from a meteorite, that was suspended from it. He was proud of the Eagle's Wings. They had been given to him by men of many nations.

The International Guild of Aeronauts had its meeting place in the city of Geneva in Switzerland. Kieron had never been further abroad from the seigneurie of Arundel than the *Marie-France* had carried him. But he knew where Switzerland was. He had looked at the maps.

Once, long ago, the newly-formed Guild of Aeronauts had sent men to him, he being the first one to reconquer the air, asking him to set down the articles of their Guild. He had thought the matter over and had been able to define only one article. He had written it for them in his own poor hand.

"The clouds and the winds are free, passing over all countries, belonging to all men. Let no man take to the skies with malice in his heart or hatred of his fellow men. On earth there are frontiers, in the sky there are none. Let those who have the good fortune to become airborne remember that the blood of all men is of one colour."

It was the first and only article required by the International Guild of Aeronauts. Any who wished to fly for other purposes than peaceful commerce were denied the lore of flight, the facilities of the airborne.

Recently, the Guild had requested Kieron to visit Geneva to receive the Eagle's Wings. Being old, he replied that he no longer felt equal to the journey, but he thanked them for their kindness, none the less.

If the Cloud Walker was unable to visit Geneva, the International Guild of Aeronauts was not unable to visit Arundel. They came, two thousand of them, in ten helium airships. They came, bearing gifts, speaking many languages.

There were Indians, Africans, Frenchmen, Germans, Russians, Americans, Chinese and many nationalities of which Kieron had not even heard. The numbers swelled as men journeyed from all parts of Britain.

In the end, four thousand men stood with bared heads in pouring rain, while the Cloud Walker sat in his wheeled chair under canvas and listened to speeches in many languages.

He understood from the British and American speeches what all these young men were saying. He was overwhelmed by their honour. The Cloud Walker had become more than a man: he had become a symbol.

When he had his first weakness of the heart, the doctors whisked him away from the conference and prescribed complete rest.

So now here he was in the rose garden, luxuriating in

the scent of *Madame Petrina*, gazing with the fondness of memory at the small white roses called *Alyx*.

Kieron Joinerson, no longer known by that name, but known simply as Seigneur Kieron or the Cloud Walker, was content.

The Rome dirigible had passed over the rose garden. Somewhere above the Pacific Ocean, heading for Japan, Jason, son of Kieron and Petrina, was attending to his duties.

A doctor came from the castle to take one of his periodic checks on his illustrious patient. As he approached the wheeled chair, he heard a great sigh. Then he saw the body slacken.

The Cloud Walker was seventy-eight years old. In his last moments he had remembered many things. The sound of bees in childhood, the thin voice of a master painter, *Mistress Fitzalan's Leap*, the touch of Petrina, the first cry of a first child.

And he remembered Aylwin also, and the shark of the sky, and Capitaine Girod, and Kentigern, and Bruno, with his obsession of streamed lines. And he remembered the floating dandelion seeds, the whirling leaves of autumn, and all the butterflies of childhood.

Whatever, as the doctor confirmed, he died peacefully. The Cloud Walker had believed only that life was for the living. But who shall say that his spirit has not reached out to the stars?

ALSO AVAILABLE IN CORONET BOOKS

EDMUND COOPER

16217 1	Kronk	35p
04364 4	A Far Sunset	35p
02860 2	All Fool's Day	35p
17860 4	The Overman Culture	35p
18614 3	Who Needs Men?	35p
10904 1	Five To Twelve	35p
15132 3	The Uncertain Midnight	25p
15091 2	The Last Continent	25p
16464 6	Transit	30p
12975 1	Sea-Horse In The Sky	30p

RICHARD AVERY

19472 3	The Expendables: The Deathworms of Kratos	35p

All these books are available at your bookshop or newsagent, or can be ordered direct from the publisher. Just tick the titles you want and fill in the form below.

- -

CORONET BOOKS, P.O. Box 11, Falmouth, Cornwall.
Please send cheque or postal order. No currency, and allow the following for postage and packing:
1 book–10p, 2 books–15p, 3 books–20p, 4–5 books–25p, 6–9 books–4p per copy, 10–15 books–2½p per copy, over 30 books free within the U.K.
Overseas–please allow 10p for the first book and 5p per copy for each additional book.

Name ....

Address ....

....